Evaluation Masters

Applications and Connections

Course 2

McGraw-Hill

New York, New York
Columbus, Ohio
Mission Hills, California
Peoria, Illinois

Send all inquiries to:
Glencoe/McGraw-Hill
936 Eastwind Drive
Westerville, OH 43081

ISBN: 0-02-824606-3

3 4 5 6 7 8 9 10 POH 02 01 00 99 98 97 96 95

CONTENTS

Chapter	Title	Page
1	Test, Form 1A	1–2
1	Test, Form 1B	3–4
1	Test, Form 2A	5
1	Test, Form 2B	6
1	Quiz A (1-1 through 1-5)	7
1	Quiz B (1-6 through 1-10)	7
1	Cumulative Review	8
1	Cumulative Test	9
2	Test, Form 1A	10–11
2	Test, Form 1B	12–13
2	Test, Form 2A	14
2	Test, Form 2B	15
2	Quiz A (2-1 through 2-5)	16
2	Quiz B (2-6 through 2-10)	16
2	Cumulative Review	17
2	Cumulative Test	18
3	Test, Form 1A	19–20
3	Test, Form 1B	21–22
3	Test, Form 2A	23
3	Test, Form 2B	24
3	Quiz A (3-1 through 3-4)	25
3	Quiz B (3-5 through 3-8)	25
3	Cumulative Review	26
3	Cumulative Test	27
4	Test, Form 1A	28–29
4	Test, Form 1B	30–31
4	Test, Form 2A	32
4	Test, Form 2B	33
4	Quiz A (4-1 through 4-5)	34
4	Quiz B (4-6 through 4-10)	34
4	Cumulative Review	35
4	Cumulative Test	36
5	Test, Form 1A	37–38
5	Test, Form 1B	39–40
5	Test, Form 2A	41
5	Test, Form 2B	42
5	Quiz A (5-1 through 5-6)	43
5	Quiz B (5-7 through 5-11)	43
5	Cumulative Review	44
5	Cumulative Test	45
6	Test, Form 1A	46–47
6	Test, Form 1B	48–49
6	Test, Form 2A	50
6	Test, Form 2B	51
6	Quiz A (6-1 through 6-4)	52
6	Quiz B (6-5 through 6-7)	52
6	Cumulative Review	53
6	Cumulative Test	54
7	Test, Form 1A	55–56
7	Test, Form 1B	57–58
7	Test, Form 2A	59
7	Test, Form 2B	60
7	Quiz A (7-1 through 7-5)	61
7	Quiz B (7-6 through 7-10)	61
7	Cumulative Review	62
7	Cumulative Test	63
8	Test, Form 1A	64–65
8	Test, Form 1B	66–67
8	Test, Form 2A	68
8	Test, Form 2B	69
8	Quiz A (8-1 through 8-4)	70
8	Quiz B (8-5 through 8-8)	70
8	Cumulative Review	71
8	Cumulative Test	72
9	Test, Form 1A	73–74
9	Test, Form 1B	75–76
9	Test, Form 2A	77
9	Test, Form 2B	78
9	Quiz A (9-1 through 9-5)	79
9	Quiz B (9-6 through 9-9)	79
9	Cumulative Review	80
9	Cumulative Test	81
10	Test, Form 1A	82–83
10	Test, Form 1B	84–85
10	Test, Form 2A	86
10	Test, Form 2B	87
10	Quiz A (10-1 through 10-4)	88
10	Quiz B (10-5 through 10-7)	88
10	Cumulative Review	89
10	Cumulative Test	90
11	Test, Form 1A	91–92
11	Test, Form 1B	93–94
11	Test, Form 2A	95
11	Test, Form 2B	96
11	Quiz A (11-1 through 11-5)	97
11	Quiz B (11-6 through 11-10)	97
11	Cumulative Review	98
11	Cumulative Test	99
12	Test, Form 1A	100–101
12	Test, Form 1B	102–103
12	Test, Form 2A	104
12	Test, Form 2B	105
12	Quiz A (12-1 through 12-5)	106
12	Quiz B (12-6 through 12-9)	106
12	Cumulative Review	107
12	Cumulative Test	108

Chapter	Title	Page
13	Test, Form 1A	109–110
13	Test, Form 1B	111–112
13	Test, Form 2A	113
13	Test, Form 2B	114
13	Quiz A (13-1 through 13-4)	115
13	Quiz B (13-5 through 13-8)	115
13	Cumulative Review	116
13	Cumulative Test	117
14	Test, Form 1A	118–119
14	Test, Form 1B	120–121
14	Test, Form 2A	122
14	Test, Form 2B	123
14	Quiz A (14-1 through 14-3)	124
14	Quiz B (14-4 through 14-6)	124
14	Cumulative Review	125
14	Cumulative Test	126

Semester Tests

Semester Test, Form 1	127–130
Semester Test, Form 2	131–133

Final Tests

Final Test, Form 1	134–138
Final Test, Form 2	139–141

Answers ... 142–188

Form 1A

1. Estimate $6{,}235 + 2{,}505$. Use rounding.
   A. 12,000   B. 10,000   C. 9,000   D. 8,000

   1. _____

2. Estimate $7{,}623 - 4{,}317$. Use rounding.
   A. 11,900   B. 3,000   C. 4,000   D. 5,300

   2. _____

3. Estimate the difference of 28,624 and 14,219.
   A. 14,000   B. 16,000   C. 4,400   D. 42,800

   3. _____

4. Estimate 551×6. Use patterns.
   A. 8,000   B. 3,600   C. 4,000   D. 3,000

   4. _____

5. Estimate the quotient of 9,497 and 28. Use patterns.
   A. 90   B. 900   C. 300   D. 30

   5. _____

6. Is $68 + 41 = 109$ reasonable?
   A. yes   B. no

   6. _____

7. Is $795 - 698 = 107$ reasonable?
   A. yes   B. no

   7. _____

8. Evaluate $5 \cdot 7 + 9 \cdot 6$.
   A. 480   B. 176   C. 54.72   D. 89

   8. _____

9. Evaluate $10 + (72 + 28) \div 50$.
   A. 12   B. 2.2   C. 14   D. 20

   9. _____

10. Evaluate $15(4 - 1) \div 5 + 5$.
    A. 6   B. 14   C. 4.5   D. 41

    10. _____

11. Evaluate $81 \div 9 + 33 - 5$.
    A. 757   B. 2   C. 37   D. 3

    11. _____

12. Evaluate $a + b - c$ if $a = 8$, $b = 3$, and $c = 5$.
    A. 6   B. 16   C. 0   D. 10

    12. _____

13. Evaluate $3ab$ if $a = 8$ and $b = 3$.
    A. 27   B. 14   C. 15   D. 72

    13. _____

14. Evaluate $\frac{3a}{4} - c$ if $a = 8$ and $c = 6$.
    A. 2   B. 0   C. 1   D. $\frac{3}{4}$

    14. _____

15. Write 7^3 as a product.
    A. $3 \cdot 3 \cdot 3$ B. $7 \cdot 7$
    C. $3 \cdot 3 \cdot 3 \cdot 3$ D. $7 \cdot 7 \cdot 7$

    15. _____

Chapter 1 Test, Form 1A (continued)

16. Write $8 \cdot 8 \cdot 8 \cdot 8$ using exponents.
   A. 4^8 **B.** 8^8 **C.** 8^4 **D.** 4^4

16. _____

17. Evaluate 2^6.
   A. 12   **B.** 64   **C.** 32   **D.** 26

17. _____

18. Solve $m - 16 = 53$.
   A. 69   **B.** 37   **C.** 213   **D.** 848

18. _____

19. Solve $17k = 153$.
   A. 170   **B.** 136   **C.** 2,601   **D.** 9

19. _____

20. Solve $\frac{e}{8} = 16$.
   A. 2   **B.** 128   **C.** 8   **D.** 28

20. _____

21. Solve $16 + y = 64$.
   A. 48   **B.** 4   **C.** 80   **D.** 1,204

21. _____

22. The Donovans traveled 850 miles to New York City to attend a wedding. They took a different route home and traveled 915 miles. How many more miles did they travel on the way home?
   A. 915 mi   **B.** 65 mi   **C.** 135 mi   **D.** 75 mi

22. _____

23. Use each of the digits 5, 6, 7, 8, and 9 once to form a two-digit number and a three-digit number that when multiplied have the least product possible. What is this product?
   A. 44,184   **B.** 39,463   **C.** 39,372   **D.** 39,273

23. _____

24. Four boys share a large pizza. The medium size costs $6. The large size costs more than the medium size. How much did each boy pay?
   A. $1.50   **B.** $1.25
   C. $1.75   **D.** missing facts

24. _____

25. Cal has $8.75. Len has three times as much except for $10 less. How much money does Len have?
   A. $8.25   **B.** $16.25
   C. $17   **D.** missing facts

25. _____

BONUS Solve $\frac{k}{3} = \frac{2}{9}$.

_____

   A. $\frac{2}{27}$ **B.** $\frac{2}{3}$ **C.** $1\frac{1}{2}$ **D.** $13\frac{1}{2}$

Form 1B

1. Estimate $8.00 + $5.68 + $1.42. Use rounding.
   A. $18.00   B. $15.00   C. $16.00   D. $17.00

   1. _____

2. Estimate 12,745 − 7,285. Use rounding.
   A. 6,000   B. 5,000   C. 4,000   D. 6,500

   2. _____

3. Estimate the sum of 16,016 and 12,153. Use rounding.
   A. 30,000   B. 27,999   C. 28,000   D. 29,000

   3. _____

4. Estimate 491 ÷ 31. Use patterns.
   A. 16   B. 15   C. 14   D. 17

   4. _____

5. Estimate the product of 8,167 and 52. Use patterns.
   A. 40,000   B. 320,000   C. 400,000   D. 32,000

   5. _____

6. Is $4.67 + $0.53 = $8.20 reasonable?
   A. yes   B. no

   6. _____

7. Is 886 − 328 = 558 reasonable?
   A. yes   B. no

   7. _____

8. Evaluate $3 \cdot 9 + 4 \cdot 8$.
   A. 59   B. 47   C. 312   D. 95

   8. _____

9. Evaluate $12 + (65 + 35) \div 25$.
   A. 4.48   B. 44.8   C. 16   D. 448

   9. _____

10. Evaluate $16(3-1) \div 4 + 4$
    A. 4   B. 2.25   C. 3   D. 12

    10. _____

11. Evaluate $72 \div 8 + 19 - 11$.
    A. 17   B. 4.5   C. 39   D. 88

    11. _____

12. Evaluate $c - b - a$ if $a = 2$, $b = 5$, and $c = 9$.
    A. 2   B. 6   C. 3   D. 5

    12. _____

13. Evaluate $4ab$ if $a = 7$ and $b = 5$.
    A. 48   B. 140   C. 150   D. 50

    13. _____

14. Evaluate $\frac{2a}{5} - b$ if $a = 10$ and $b = 4$.
    A. 0   B. 1   C. 2.4   D. 2

    14. _____

Chapter 1 Test Form 1B (continued)

15. Write 4^3 as a product. **15.** _____
  A. $3 \cdot 3 \cdot 3$ **B.** $4 \cdot 4 \cdot 4$ **C.** $4 \cdot 4$ **D.** $3 \cdot 3 \cdot 3 \cdot 3$

16. Write $3 \cdot 3 \cdot 3 \cdot 3 \cdot 3$ using exponents. **16.** _____
  A. 5^2 **B.** 3^4 **C.** 5^3 **D.** 3^5

17. Evaluate 11^4. **17.** _____
  A. 44 **B.** 161,051 **C.** 1,331 **D.** 14,641

18. Solve $19 = l - 16$. **18.** _____
  A. 304 **B.** 53 **C.** 35 **D.** 3

19. Solve $13p = 104$. **19.** _____
  A. 8 **B.** 91 **C.** 1,352 **D.** 117

20. Solve $\frac{m}{7} = 14$. **20.** _____
  A. 2 **B.** 98 **C.** 7 **D.** 0.5

21. Solve $75 = 19 + e$. **21.** _____
  A. 4 **B.** 1,425 **C.** 56 **D.** 94

22. Susan is solving problems in Chapter 6. There are 8 lessons **22.** _____
  with 25 problems in each lesson. How many problems does
  Susan have to solve?
  A. 175 **B.** 17 **C.** 33 **D.** 200

23. Use each of the digits 5, 6, 7, 8, and 9 once to make a two- **23.** _____
  digit number and a three-digit number that when multiplied
  have the greatest product possible. What is the product?
  A. 86,625 **B.** 84,000 **C.** 83,905 **D.** 74,790

24. There are 358 students that will take a test in the cafeteria. **24.** _____
  If each table seats 12 students, how many tables are needed?
  A. 29 **B.** 28 **C.** 30 **D.** 35

25. A trip from Los Angeles to New York City is 3,000 miles. If **25.** _____
  125 gallons of gasoline are used, how many miles per gallon
  is this?
  A. 24 **B.** 20 **C.** 30 **D.** 25

BONUS Find the last digit of 9^{10} without computing. _____
  A. 10 **B.** 9 **C.** 0 **D.** 1

Form 2A _____

Estimate. Use rounding.

1. $12,833 - 8,675$
2. $5,285 + 6,287 + 7,244$
3. sum of $2,899$ and $11,208$
4. difference of $8,742$ and $5,336$

Estimate. Use patterns.

5. $798 \div 4$
6. $5,807 \times 30$

Determine whether the answers shown are reasonable.

7. $397 + 598 = 995$
8. $702 - 96 = 606$
9. The sum of 55 and 348 is 503.
10. The difference of 916 and 586 is 330.

Evaluate each expression.

11. $36 \div (8 - 5)$
12. $(44 + 55) \div 9 + 9$

Evaluate each expression if a = 8, b = 4, and c = 2.

13. $2b - c$
14. $3(a + b) - c$
15. Write 7^4 as a product.
16. Write $11 \cdot 11$ using exponents.

Evaluate.

17. 10^4
18. 9 squared

Solve each equation.

19. $16x = 144$
20. $l - 39 = 128$
21. $29 + z = 117$
22. $\frac{m}{7} = 22$

Solve each problem.

23. Will $50.00 buy a pair of running shoes at $46.95 and a pair of socks at $4.00?
24. In the 1986–1987 and 1987–1988 seasons, Larry Bird scored 4,351 points in basketball for the Boston Celtics. In the 1986–1987 season, he scored 2,076 points. How many more points did he score in the 1987–1988 season?
25. There are 10 audio-tape cassettes in a package for $15.95. How much will 40 cassettes cost?

BONUS Evaluate $2(5-2) \div ((6 - 3)6)$.

1. _____
2. _____
3. _____
4. _____
5. _____
6. _____
7. _____
8. _____
9. _____
10. _____
11. _____
12. _____
13. _____
14. _____
15. _____
16. _____
17. _____
18. _____
19. _____
20. _____
21. _____
22. _____
23. _____
24. _____
25. _____

_____

Glencoe Division, Macmillan/McGraw-Hill

Chapter 1 Test

Form 2B _____

Estimate. Use rounding.

1. $24,856 - 12,978$
2. $6,186 + 4,389 + 8,347$
3. sum of 9,175 and 4,893
4. difference of 7,931 and 3,275

Estimate. Use patterns.

5. $6,308 \times 9$ 6. $8,219 \div 88$

Determine whether the answers shown are reasonable.

7. $\$4.79 + \$1.41 = \$6.90$ 8. $712 - 189 = 523$
9. The sum of 178 and 33 is 211.   10. The difference of 896 and 438 is 458.

Evaluate each expression.

11. $(25 - 9) - 5 \times 3$ 12. $(19 - 7) \div 3 + 9$

Evaluate each expression if a = 10, b = 6, and c = 4.

13. $3b - a$ 14. $2(b + c) - a$
15. Write 6^5 as a product.
16. Write $11 \cdot 11 \cdot 11 \cdot 11$ using exponents.

Evaluate.

17. 12^3 18. 4 squared

Solve each equation.

19. $64 = l - 36$ 20. $19p = 171$
21. $m + 41 = 80$ 22. $\frac{r}{3} = 35$

If the problem has enough facts, solve it. If not, write the missing facts.

23. Sanchez bought a sandwich for \$3.95 and an orange juice for \$0.75. How much change did he get from a \$10 bill?
24. The distance between successive bases on a baseball diamond is about 27.43 meters. About how far does a player run when hitting a double?
25. A VCR and a television set each cost the same. What is the total cost for the two items?

BONUS Evaluate $2 [2(6 + 3) \div ((6 - 3)2)]$.

1. _____
2. _____
3. _____
4. _____
5. _____
6. _____
7. _____
8. _____
9. _____
10. _____
11. _____
12. _____
13. _____
14. _____
15. _____
16. _____
17. _____
18. _____
19. _____
20. _____
21. _____
22. _____
23. _____
24. _____
25. _____
_____

Use with Lessons 1-1 through 1-5 ▄▄▄▄▄▄▄▄

Estimate. Use rounding.

1. $9,429 - 3,158$ 2. $622 + 9,102 + 4,723$

Estimate. Use patterns.

3. $8,198 \times 9$ 4. $635 \div 28$

Determine whether the answers shown are reasonable.

5. $696 + 129 = 825$ 6. $3,000 - 1,868 = 2,132$

7. The sum of 357 and 143 is 700.

8. The difference of 601 and 237 is 364.

9. Will $50.00 buy a pair of in-line roller blades at $34.99 and a set of elbow-knee pads at $14.99?

10. Jamie has $9.75. Jenny has twice as much except for one dollar less. How much do they have in all?

1. _____
2. _____
3. _____
4. _____
5. _____
6. _____
7. _____
8. _____
9. _____
10. _____

Use with Lessons 1-6 through 1-10 ▄▄▄▄▄▄▄▄

Evaluate each expression.

1. $14 - 6 \div 2 + 8$ 2. $(38 - 8) - 5 \times 6$

Evaluate each expression if a = 5, b = 3, and c = 4.

3. $2a - 3b$ 4. $a(c + b) - c$

5. Write 8^5 as a product.

6. Write $25 \cdot 25$ using exponents.

7. Name the number that is a solution of $15t = 240$; 16, 17, 18.

Solve each equation.

8. $\frac{m}{10} = 3$ 9. $f + 19 = 43$

If this problem has enough facts, solve it. If not, write the missing facts.

10. Sara pays $2 a pair more for striped socks than for solid socks. How many pairs of striped socks can she buy for $14?

1. _____
2. _____
3. _____
4. _____
5. _____
6. _____
7. _____
8. _____
9. _____
10. _____

Cumulative Review Chapter 1

Estimate. Use rounding. (Lesson 1-2)

1. $10{,}645 - 5{,}283$
2. $3{,}185 + 8{,}389 + 6{,}404$
3. sum of 5,789 and 7,316
4. difference of 7,742 and 4,227

Estimate. Use patterns. (Lesson 1-3)

5. $689 \div 7$
6. $7{,}895 \times 4$

Determine whether the answers shown are reasonable. (Lesson 1-4)

7. $298 + 497 = 895$
8. $603 - 97 = 556$
9. The sum of 48 and 255 is 323.
10. The difference of 816 and 486 is 330.

Evaluate each expression. (Lesson 1-7)

11. $48 \div (12 - 8)$
12. $(33 + 66) \div 9 - 9$

Evaluate each expression if a = 6, b = 4, and c = 2. (Lesson 1-8)

13. $3a - c$
14. $2(b + c) - a$
15. Write 8^3 as a product. (Lesson 1-9)
16. Write $3 \cdot 3 \cdot 3 \cdot 3 \cdot 3$ using exponents. (Lesson 1-9)

Evaluate each expression. (Lesson 1-9)

17. 7^4
18. 5 squared

Solve each equation. (Lesson 1-10)

19. $17a = 136$
20. $b - 42 = 59$
21. $39 + c = 121$
22. $\frac{d}{6} = 34$

Solve each problem. (Lessons 1-1, 1-5, 1-6)

23. Will $50.00 buy a dozen golf balls at $21.95 and a sweater at $28.50?
24. Use each of the digits 1, 2, 3, and 4 exactly once to make a two-digit number and another two-digit number that when multiplied have the greatest product possible. What is the product?
25. There are 10 CDs in a box. Each CD sells for $14.95. How much will a dozen CDs cost?

1. _____
2. _____
3. _____
4. _____
5. _____
6. _____
7. _____
8. _____
9. _____
10. _____
11. _____
12. _____
13. _____
14. _____
15. _____
16. _____
17. _____
18. _____
19. _____
20. _____
21. _____
22. _____
23. _____
24. _____
25. _____

Name _____ **Date** _____

Estimate. Use rounding.

1. $1,359 + 3,709$	**A.** 4,100	**B.** 4,000	**C.** 5,200	**D.** 5,000	**1.** _____
2. $9,713 - 5,418$	**A.** 9,300	**B.** 5,300	**C.** 6,000	**D.** 5,000	**2.** _____
3. difference of 38,524 and 13,193	**A.** 27,000	**B.** 25,000	**C.** 26,000	**D.** 24,000	**3.** _____

Estimate. Use patterns.

4. $671 \div 68$	**A.** 20	**B.** 10	**C.** 30	**D.** 100	**4.** _____
5. product of 8,135 and 36	**A.** 300,000	**B.** 320,000	**C.** 240,000	**D.** 360,000	**5.** _____

Determine whether the answers shown are reasonable.

6. $895 - 598 = 397$	**A.** yes	**B.** no	**6.** _____
7. The sum of 61 and 48 is 109.	**A.** yes	**B.** no	**7.** _____

Evaluate each expression.

8. $3 \cdot 9 + 8 \cdot 7$	**A.** 357	**B.** 1,512	**C.** 457	**D.** 83	**8.** _____
9. $8 + (56 + 44) \div 25$	**A.** 4.32	**B.** 43.2	**C.** 12	**D.** 432	**9.** _____
10. $16(4 - 2) \div 8 + 7$	**A.** 11	**B.** 2.13	**C.** 28	**D.** 3	**10.** _____
11. $(49 - 7) \div 21 + 17$	**A.** 34	**B.** 19	**C.** 1.1	**D.** 1.11	**11.** _____
12. 2^7	**A.** 128	**B.** 64	**C.** 256	**D.** 14	**12.** _____

Evaluate each expression if $a = 7$, $b = 5$, and $c = 3$.

13. $a - b + c$	**A.** 2	**B.** 1	**C.** 5	**D.** 15	**13.** _____
14. $4ac$	**A.** 140	**B.** 84	**C.** 60	**D.** 15	**14.** _____
15. $2c \div 3 - 2$	**A.** 0	**B.** 2	**C.** 3	**D.** 1	**15.** _____
16. Write 1^4 as as a product.	**A.** $1 \cdot 1 \cdot 1 \cdot 1$	**B.** $4 \cdot 4 \cdot 4 \cdot 4$	**C.** $1 \cdot 4$	**D.** $4 \cdot 1$	**16.** _____
17. Write $9 \cdot 9 \cdot 9 \cdot 9 \cdot 9$ using exponents.	**A.** 5^9	**B.** 9^4	**C.** 59,049	**D.** 9^5	**17.** _____

Solve each equation.

18. $a - 12 = 79$	**A.** 67	**B.** 91	**C.** 6	**D.** 81	**18.** _____
19. $12b = 132$	**A.** 12	**B.** 10	**C.** 11	**D.** 13	**19.** _____
20. $18 + c = 31$	**A.** 13	**B.** 49	**C.** 2	**D.** 558	**20.** _____
21. $d + 48 = 78$	**A.** 30	**B.** 20	**C.** 40	**D.** 126	**21.** _____
22. $e \div 5 = 23$	**A.** 28	**B.** 115	**C.** 116	**D.** 18	**22.** _____
23. $80 = f - 27$	**A.** 53	**B.** 43	**C.** 97	**D.** 107	**23.** _____

24. Len has $8.50. Cal has twice as much except for ten dollars less. How much does Cal have?   **24.** _____
   A. $17.00   **B.** $7.00   **C.** $10.25   **D.** $10.00

25. There are 424 students who will take a test in the cafeteria. How many tables are needed?   **25.** _____
   A. 36   **B.** 53   **C.** 25   **D.** missing facts

Form 1A

Chapter 2 Test

1. Order 0.8, 0.07, 1.03, and 0.87 from least to greatest.   **1.** _____
   A. 0.07, 0.8, 1.03, 0.87   **B.** 0.07, 0.8, 0.87, 1.03
   C. 1.03, 0.87, 0.8, 0.07   **D.** 0.07, 0.87, 0.8, 1.03

Round each number to the underlined place-value position.

2. 8,2<u>0</u>5.6   **2.** _____
   A. 8,206   **B.** 8,200   **C.** 8,210   **D.** 8,205

3. 1.2<u>4</u>31   **3.** _____
   A. 1.243   **B.** 1.250   **C.** 1.241   **D.** 1.24

Estimate. Use an appropriate strategy.

4. 9.39 + 5.81   **4.** _____
   A. 15   **B.** 14   **C.** 16   **D.** 13

5. 16.42 − 9.75   **5.** _____
   A. 7   **B.** 6   **C.** 5   **D.** 8

6. 4.87 × 49.7   **6.** _____
   A. 200   **B.** 20   **C.** 250   **D.** 25

7. $6.1\overline{)71.77}$ **7.** _____
   A. 11   **B.** 10   **C.** 13   **D.** 12

Multiply or divide.

8. 4.6 × 0.24   **8.** _____
   A. 11.04   **B.** 1   **C.** 110.4   **D.** 1.104

9. 0.032 × 23   **9.** _____
   A. 0.736   **B.** 73.6   **C.** 7.36   **D.** 736

10. 0.53 × 0.003   **10.** _____
   A. 0.00122   **B.** 0.0016   **C.** 0.0015   **D.** 0.00159

11. 1.78 × 2.5   **11.** _____
   A. 4.45   **B.** 6   **C.** 4   **D.** 0.445

12. 0.0793×10^6 **12.** _____
   A. 793   **B.** 0.0008   **C.** 79,300   **D.** 7,930

13. $1.3\overline{)169}$ **13.** _____
   A. 130   **B.** 13   **C.** 1.3   **D.** 0.13

14. $0.8\overline{)0.048}$ **14.** _____
   A. 0.05   **B.** 6   **C.** 0.06   **D.** 0.6

Chapter 2 Test Form 1A (continued)

15. Find the quotient when 7.83 is divided by 0.9.
    A. 7.8   **B.** 78   **C.** 780   **D.** 8.7

15. _____

16. How many nickels are there in $25.50?
    A. 510   **B.** 500   **C.** 5,100   **D.** 51

16. _____

17. Divide $0.075\overline{)0.341}$. Round to the nearest hundredth.
    A. 4.25   **B.** 4.55   **C.** 4.54   **D.** 4.26

17. _____

18. Write 498,000 in scientific notation.
    A. 49.8×10^4 **B.** 4.98×10^6
    C. 4.98×10^5 **D.** 0.498×10^6

18. _____

19. Write 2.04×10^4 in standard form.
    A. 20,400   **B.** 2,040   **C.** 204   **D.** 204,000

19. _____

20. Complete 0.75 L = ■ mL.
    A. 75   **B.** 750   **C.** 7,500   **D.** 7.5

20. _____

21. Complete 7,462 g = ■ kg.
    A. 74.62   **B.** 0.7462   **C.** 746.2   **D.** 7.462

21. _____

22. A beaker contains 625 milliliters of water. A chemist pours 0.25 liters of the water into a solution. How many milliliters are left in the beaker?
    A. 375   **B.** 600   **C.** 2,500   **D.** 250

22. _____

23. Lee buys 100 postcards for his business. If each postcard costs 19¢, how much did he spend?
    A. $1.90   **B.** $19   **C.** $190   **D.** $19.90

23. _____

24. A giant tortoise can travel at a speed of about 0.2 kilometers per hour. At this rate, how far can it travel in 2 hours 30 minutes?
    A. 0.5 m   **B.** 12.5 m   **C.** 12.5 km   **D.** 0.5 km

24. _____

25. The trail up to the top of Pike's Peak is about 23 miles long. The Kalman family drove about three quarters of the way. About how many more miles must they drive to reach the top?
    A. 4   **B.** 8   **C.** 6   **D.** 14

25. _____

BONUS It is about 2.39×10^5 miles from Earth to our moon, and about 9.3×10^7 miles from Earth to the sun. How many times farther is it to the sun than to the moon?
    A. 389   **B.** 186   **C.** 4   **D.** 18.6

_____

Chapter 2 Test

Form 1B _____

1. Order 6.24, 6.08, 6.009, and 0.6 from least to greatest.   1. _____
   A. 0.6, 6.009, 6.08, 6.24   **B.** 6.24, 6.009, 6.08, 0.6
   C. 6.24, 6.08, 6.009, 0.6   **D.** 0.6, 6.08, 6.009, 6.24

Round each number to the underlined place-value position.

2. 3.0<u>5</u>91   2. _____
   A. 3.06   **B.** 3.059   **C.** 3.05   **D.** 3.1

3. 0.<u>7</u>519   3. _____
   A. 0.7   **B.** 0.75   **C.** 0.752   **D.** 0.8

Estimate. Use an appropriate strategy.

4. 18.75 + 6.16   4. _____
   A. 24   **B.** 27   **C.** 23   **D.** 25

5. 19.598 − 9.698   5. _____
   A. 8   **B.** 10   **C.** 11   **D.** 7

6. 42.8 × 57.7   6. _____
   A. 2,600   **B.** 2,400   **C.** 2,300   **D.** 240

7. $2.4\overline{)0.84}$ 7. _____
   A. 0.4   **B.** 0.5   **C.** 0.3   **D.** 0.6

Multiply or divide.

8. 0.61 × 2.9   8. _____
   A. 3   **B.** 2.03   **C.** 1.769   **D.** 2.30

9. 25 × 0.096   9. _____
   A. 2.5   **B.** 25   **C.** 2.4   **D.** 24

10. 0.001 × 0.567   10. _____
    A. 567   **B.** 0.5   **C.** 0.567   **D.** 0.000567

11. 10^4 × 2.0503   11. _____
    A. 20,503   **B.** 2,050.3   **C.** 205   **D.** 205,030

12. $3.6\overline{)18.036}$ 12. _____
    A. 4.5   **B.** 5.01   **C.** 4.05   **D.** 5.1

13. $0.16\overline{)0.256}$ 13. _____
    A. 0.2   **B.** 1.8   **C.** 1.6   **D.** 1.7

14. $0.038\overline{)0.456}$ 14. _____
    A. 12   **B.** 21   **C.** 13   **D.** 15

Chapter 2 Test Form 1B (continued)

15. Find the quotient when 117.99 is divided by 6.9.
 A. 17   **B.** 17.1   **C.** 1.7   **D.** 1.07

15. _____

16. How many quarters are there in $50?
 A. 20   **B.** 175   **C.** 2,000   **D.** 200

16. _____

17. Divide $4.2\overline{)2.663}$. Round to the nearest hundredth.
 A. 0.60   **B.** 0.63   **C.** 0.634   **D.** 0.50

17. _____

18. Write 73,450 in scientific notation.
 A. 73.450×10^3 **B.** 73.450×10^4
 C. 7.345×10^3 **D.** 7.345×10^4

18. _____

19. Write 9.73×10^2 in standard form.
 A. 973   **B.** 97.3   **C.** 9,730   **D.** 97,300

19. _____

20. Complete 3.64 kg = ■ g.
 A. 364   **B.** 36.4   **C.** 3,640   **D.** 0.364

20. _____

21. Complete 2,725 m = ■ km.
 A. 272.5   **B.** 2.725   **C.** 27.25   **D.** 0.2725

21. _____

22. A part-time job in a coffee shop pays $4.75 an hour. How much would you earn in 10 hours?
 A. $47   **B.** $475   **C.** $4.75   **D.** $47.50

22. _____

23. The Lincolns pay $3,540 in property taxes a year. What is the cost each week for property taxes. Round up to the next cent.
 A. $9.70   **B.** $68.08   **C.** $29.50   **D.** $295

23. _____

24. Ken walked 3.5 miles more than Gerry. If Ken walked 11.25 miles, how many miles did Gerry walk?
 A. 14.75 mi **B.** 15 mi **C.** 7 mi   **D.** 7.75 mi

24. _____

25. Myra vacationed for 3 days and 2 nights. She spent $72 a night for a motel and $35 a day for food. How much more did she spend on lodging than on food?
 A. $144   **B.** $105   **C.** $41   **D.** $39

25. _____

BONUS On a balance scale a cement block balances with a 10.5-pound weight and one half of the same size cement block. How much does the cement block weigh?
 A. 21 lb   **B.** 5.25 lb   **C.** 12.5 lb   **D.** 15 lb

_____

Form 2A

Order each set of numbers from least to greatest.

1. 0.68, 1.01, 0.99, 0.7

2. 10.44, 1.173, 10.4, 10.006

Round each number to the underlined place-value position.

3. 215.0$\underline{1}$8

4. 0.$\underline{6}$941

5. 1$\underline{0}$.096

6. 3.0$\underline{5}$12

Estimate. Use an appropriate strategy.

7. 8.76 + 6.74

8. 12.31 − 9.33

9. 32.8 × 49.3

10. 4.2$\overline{)0.78}$

Multiply or divide.

11. 3.9 × 10,000

12. 6.4 × 0.003

13. 0.00029 × 10^7

14. 0.6$\overline{)5.4}$

15. How many dimes are there in $45.00?

Change from standard form to scientific notation or vice-versa.

16. 4.09 × 10^3

17. 795

Complete.

18. 2.93 L = ■ mL

19. 432 g = ■ kg

20. Divide 0.04$\overline{)0.0853}$. Round to the nearest hundredth.

21. During a twelve-week period, Raman saved $10.25 per week. Estimate the amount he saved in twelve weeks.

22. To make punch, Lawrence mixes 3 L of lemon soda with 2,800 mL of orange juice. How many liters of punch does this make?

23. The O'Sullivans spend $127.75 a year for a daily newspaper. They receive it 365 days a year. How much does one paper cost?

24. Jerry hiked 4 fewer miles than Raul. If Jerry hiked 13.3 miles, how many miles did Raul hike?

25. Claudia bought 3 pounds of peanuts for $5.97, 2 packages of cheese crackers for $5.98, and 2 bags of corn chips for $2.98. Should she expect to pay about $10, $15, or $20 at the checkout?

BONUS What is the difference between 1.73 × 10^4 and 1.73 × 10^3?

1. _____

2. _____

3. _____

4. _____

5. _____

6. _____

7. _____

8. _____

9. _____

10. _____

11. _____

12. _____

13. _____

14. _____

15. _____

16. _____

17. _____

18. _____

19. _____

20. _____

21. _____

22. _____

23. _____

24. _____

25. _____

_____

Form 2B

Order each set of numbers from least to greatest.

1. 1.53, 1.74, 0.91, 0.9   **2.** 6.55, 7.501, 6.0, 7.032, 6.01

Round each number to the underlined place-value position.

3. 85.97   **4.** 0.124   **5.** 6.1501   **6.** 2.5691

Estimate. Use an appropriate strategy.

7. 42.89 − 10.16   **8.** 9.31 + 8.75

9. 22.7 × 56.2   **10.** 3.3)‾0.89‾

Multiply or divide.

11. 100,000 × 1.6   **12.** 4.7 × 0.005

13. 0.00303 × 10^8   **14.** 0.7)‾8.4‾

15. How many nickels are there in $35.00?

Change from standard form to scientific notation or vice-versa.

16. 8.9×10^5 **17.** 214

Complete.

18. 301 g = ■ kg   **19.** 0.75 L = ■ mL

20. Divide 0.07)‾0.389‾. Round to the nearest hundredth.

21. Ben bought 18 yards of fabric to make draperies. The fabric cost $5.35 a yard. Estimate the cost of the fabric.

22. Chico made 4 L of punch for a party. If he served 3,250 mL of punch, how many liters of punch were left?

23. Kari works 12 hours a week. She earns $5.25 an hour. How much does she earn in two weeks?

24. Mr. Tsao needs a 45.5-centimeter piece of molding. How many centimeters remain after he cut off the end of a 1-meter piece of molding?

25. Vicki vacationed for 7 days and 6 nights. She spent $98 a night for the hotel and $40 a day for food. How much did she spend on food and lodging?

BONUS Use scientific notation to show the product of 1.73×10^{20} and 1.73×10^6.

1. _____

2. _____

3. _____

4. _____

5. _____

6. _____

7. _____

8. _____

9. _____

10. _____

11. _____

12. _____

13. _____

14. _____

15. _____

16. _____

17. _____

18. _____

19. _____

20. _____

21. _____

22. _____

23. _____

24. _____

25. _____

_____

(Lessons 2-1 through 2-5) ━━━━━━━━━━━━━━━━━━━━━━━

Replace each ● *with* <, >, *or* = *to make a true sentence.*

1. 0.0026 ● 0.026

2. 8.08 ● 8

Round each number to the underlined place-value position.

3. 0.9̲5   4. 1̲6.712

Estimate. Use an appropriate strategy.

5. 46.12
  + 19.6

6. 76.96
  − 34.25

Multiply.

7. 0.52
  × 18

8. 0.0032
  × 0.49

9. Multiply mentally: 414.2×10^3

10. Pears cost $1.29 a pound. How much will ten pounds cost?

1. _____
2. _____
3. _____
4. _____
5. _____
6. _____
7. _____
8. _____
9. _____
10. _____

- -

(Lessons 2-6 through 2-10) ━━━━━━━━━━━━━━━━━━━━━━━

1. The circulation of the local newspaper is about 87,500 newspapers. Write the number in scientific notation.

2. Write 7.12×10^5 in standard form.

3. Divide 0.064$)\overline{0.2944}$.

4. Find the quotient when 1.64 is divided by 0.8.

5. Divide 2.5$)\overline{7.691}$. Round to the nearest hundredth.

6. Divide 0.06$)\overline{\$26.75}$. Round up to the next cent.

7. Divide 6.5$)\overline{6,389.32}$. Round to the greatest place-value position of the quotient.

8. How many milliliters are in 0.5 liters?

9. How many centimeters are in 1.32 kilometers?

10. Cal's Cassette Corner is selling 5 blank audio cassettes for $12.50. Lenny says he can buy 25 cassettes for under $60. Is his answer reasonable? Why or why not?

1. _____
2. _____
3. _____
4. _____
5. _____
6. _____
7. _____
8. _____
9. _____
10. _____

Cumulative Review Chapters 1-2

Evaluate each expression. (Lesson 1-7)

1. $(22 + 66) \div 8 - 8$ **2.** $16(5 - 2) \div 24 + 5$

Evaluate each expression if x = 8, y = 5, and z = 4. (Lesson 1-8)

3. $2y + x$ **4.** $3z - x$

5. $3(x + y) - 1$ **6.** $2(x - z) + y$

7. Write 11^2 as a product. (Lesson 1-9)

8. Write $5 \cdot 5 \cdot 5 \cdot 5 \cdot 5 \cdot 5$ using exponents. (Lesson 1-9)

Solve each equation. (Lesson 1-10)

9. $p + 21 = 38$ **10.** $q - 18 = 49$

11. $18r = 162$ **12.** $\frac{s}{7} = 17$

13. Order 0.58, 0.91, 0.89, and 0.6 from least to greatest. (Lesson 2-1)

Estimate. Use an appropriate strategy. (Lesson 2-3)

14. 33.9×68.2 **15.** $3.7\overline{)0.81}$

Multiply or divide. (Lessons 2-4, 2-7)

16. 8.5×0.004 **17.** $0.0012\overline{)144}$

18. Divide $0.05\overline{)0.0951}$. Round to the nearest hundredth. (Lesson 2-8)

Change from standard form to scientific notation or vice versa. (Lesson 2-6)

19. 69,000,000   **20.** 8.16×10^4

Complete. (Lesson 2-9)

21. $1.58 \text{ L} = \blacksquare \text{ mL}$ **22.** $679 \text{ g} = \blacksquare \text{ kg}$

Solve. (Lessons 1-1, 1-6, 2-10)

23. Rosie walked 5 more miles than Darren. If Rosie walked 12.5 miles, how many miles did Darren walk?

24. The total cost for a compact disc player, VCR, and television set is $1,695. How much does the compact disc player cost?

25. The trail up to the top of Pike's Peak is about 23 miles. The Mareska family drove about one fourth of the way. Did they drive about 5 miles or 6 miles?

1. _____

2. _____

3. _____

4. _____

5. _____

6. _____

7. _____

8. _____

9. _____

10. _____

11. _____

12. _____

13. _____

14. _____

15. _____

16. _____

17. _____

18. _____

19. _____

20. _____

21. _____

22. _____

23. _____

24. _____

25. _____

Cumulative Test Chapters 1-2

Evaluate each expression.

1. $2(13 + 5) \div 9 + 8$ **A.** 12   **B.** 2.1   **C.** 10   **D.** 15

1. _____

Evaluate each expression if x = 3, y = 5, and z = 9.

2. $5x - z$ **A.** 7   **B.** 6   **C.** 8   **D.** 9

2. _____

3. $2(y + z) - 9$ **A.** 10   **B.** 20   **C.** 19   **D.** 21

3. _____

4. Write 2^3 as a product.
   A. $2 \cdot 2 \cdot 2$ **B.** $2 \cdot 3$ **C.** $3 \cdot 2$ **D.** $2 \cdot 2 \cdot 2 \cdot 2$

4. _____

5. Write $9 \cdot 9 \cdot 9 \cdot 9 \cdot 9 \cdot 9 \cdot 9$ using exponents.
   A. 7^9 **B.** 9^6 **C.** 7^6 **D.** 9^7

5. _____

Solve each equation.

6. $104 = 13a$ **A.** 1,352   **B.** 91   **C.** 8   **D.** 9

6. _____

7. $52 = c - 37$ **A.** 90   **B.** 15   **C.** 25   **D.** 89

7. _____

8. $\frac{d}{8} = 17$ **A.** 136   **B.** $2\frac{1}{8}$ **C.** 9   **D.** 25

8. _____

Estimate. Use an appropriate strategy.

9. $15.35 - 8.92$ **A.** 7   **B.** 6   **C.** 5   **D.** 8

9. _____

10. 21.7×49.2 **A.** 900   **B.** 1,200   **C.** 800   **D.** 1,000

10. _____

11. $5.8 \overline{)0.63}$ **A.** 1   **B.** 10   **C.** 0.01   **D.** 0.1

11. _____

Multiply or divide.

12. $10^7 \times 0.00812$ **A.** 8,120   **B.** 812   **C.** 8.12   **D.** 81,200

12. _____

13. $0.0013 \overline{)1.69}$ **A.** 1,300   **B.** 130   **C.** 13   **D.** 13,000

13. _____

14. Divide $0.03 \overline{)0.0635}$. Round to the nearest hundredth.
   A. 2.1   **B.** 2.12   **C.** 2.11   **D.** 2.10

14. _____

15. Change 25,000,000,000 to scientific notation.
   A. 2.5×10^9 **B.** 25×10^9 **C.** 25×10^{10} **D.** 2.5×10^{10}

15. _____

16. Change 2.08×10^3 to standard form.
   A. 2,080   **B.** 20,800   **C.** 208   **D.** 2,800

16. _____

17. $0.02 \text{ km} = \blacksquare \text{ m}$ **A.** 20   **B.** 200   **C.** 2   **D.** 2,000

17. _____

18. $25 \text{ kL} = \blacksquare \text{ L}$ **A.** 2,500   **B.** 250   **C.** 2.5   **D.** 25,000

18. _____

19. Oranges cost $2.39 a dozen. How much will 10 dozen cost?
   A. $23.90   **B.** $25.00   **C.** $239.00   **D.** $24.00

19. _____

20. Cosette has $10. Pam has twice as much except for two dollars less. How much do they have in all?
   A. $18.00   **B.** $8.00   **C.** $28.00   **D.** $25.00

20. _____

Glencoe Division, Macmillan/McGraw-Hill

Form 1A _____ *Chapter 3 Test*

Ricardo made a circle graph to show how he spent his time.

Ricardo's Day

study 2 h
sports 2 h
sleep 8 h
meals 2 h
school 6 h
other 4 h

1. What fraction of the day is spent sleeping?
   A. $\frac{1}{12}$ **B.** $\frac{1}{4}$ **C.** $\frac{1}{3}$ **D.** $\frac{1}{6}$

   1. _____

2. How much more time is spent in school than in sports?
   A. 1 hour **B.** 6 hours
   C. 2 hours **D.** 4 hours

   2. _____

3. What fraction of the day is spent in school or sleeping?
   A. $\frac{7}{12}$ **B.** $\frac{5}{12}$ **C.** $\frac{1}{2}$ **D.** $\frac{1}{6}$

   3. _____

The scores for a 30-point test are shown at the right. Make a frequency table.

25	17	25	17	28
25	25	28	25	17
21	24	30	21	30
26	23	28	21	20
19	25	19	24	21

4. What is the frequency of the score that appeared the most often?
   A. 4 **B.** 6 **C.** 5 **D.** 7

   4. _____

5. If 19 is the lowest passing score, how many scores are passing scores?
   A. 20 **B.** 15 **C.** 22 **D.** 19

   5. _____

6. Name the scale of the number line.
   A. 12–15 **B.** 12–39 **C.** 18–27 **D.** 12–27

   12 15 18 21 24 27

   6. _____

7. Name the interval of the number line.
   A. 2 **B.** 3 **C.** 1 **D.** 4

   7. _____

8. Find the range of 3, 4, 2, 8, 7, 5, and 6.
   A. 2 **B.** 5 **C.** 35 **D.** 6

   8. _____

Use the line plot to answer Exercises 9 and 10.

9. Name the outlier in the line plot.
   A. 0 **B.** 8 **C.** 4 **D.** 2

   0 2 4 6 8

   9. _____

10. Name the cluster in the line plot.
    A. between 0 and 4 **B.** between 0 and 8
    C. between 4 and 8 **D.** between 0 and 6

    10. _____

11. Find the mode(s) of 22, 25, 27, 28, 30, 27, and 23.
    A. 30 **B.** 25 **C.** 23 **D.** 27

    11. _____

12. Find the median of 15, 19, 20, 21, 22, 24, and 24.
    A. 21 **B.** 20 **C.** 15 **D.** 24

    12. _____

13. Find the mean of 31, 25, 20, 18, 22, and 28.
    A. 22 **B.** 24 **C.** 144 **D.** 25

    13. _____

Chapter 3 Test, Form 1A (continued)

14. Which digit in the numbers 59, 68, 67, 65, 53, 64, 65, and 70 would *not* appear as a *leaf* when drawing a stem-and-leaf plot?
   A. 0   **B.** 9   **C.** 2   **D.** 5

14. _____

The stem-and-leaf plot at the right shows the scores on a science test.

```
5 | 024
6 | 133
7 | 28999
8 | 13899
9 | 447
```

15. Name the highest score on the test.
   A. 96   **B.** 100   **C.** 94   **D.** 97

15. _____

16. Name the score that appears the most.
   A. 79   **B.** 97   **C.** 89   **D.** 98

16. _____

On the day before class elections, 50 students were asked who they would choose for the class treasurer. The graph at the right shows the results.

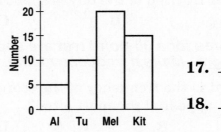
Election for Treasurer

17. Who do you think will win the election?
   A. Kit   **B.** Al   **C.** Mel   **D.** Tu

17. _____

18. Who is most likely to lose the election?
   A. Kit   **B.** Al   **C.** Mel   **D.** Tu

18. _____

Employee salaries at a company are shown in the frequency table at the right.

Salary	Number
$100,000	1
$75,000	2
$50,000	3
$24,000	15
$12,000	6

19. Which average best represents the data in the frequency table?

   A. mean   **B.** mode or median
   C. median   **D.** mode

19. _____

20. What number best describes the data?
   A. $30,815   **B.** $24,000   **C.** $18,000   **D.** $21,000

20. _____

BONUS What is the best description for the average employee at ACE Electronics?

_____

ACE Electronics	Paul Liang	Joseph Foley	Susan Keveney	Jenny Lincoln	Raman Sharma
Age	28	33	37	32	35
Salary	$13,000	$26,500	$65,000	$35,000	$48,000
Height (cm)	155	159	164	158	149
Favorite Entertainment	reading	sports	sports	theater	movies

   A. 33 years; $38,000; 157 cm; theater

   B. 32 years; $34,700; 159 cm; sports

   C. 33 years; $35,000; 157 cm; sports

   D. 34 years; $34,700; 158 cm; reading

Form 1B

The circle graph shows the favorite after-school activities of a group of students.

After-School Activities

reading 10 · sports 15 · visit friends 20 · music 25 · television 30

1. What fraction of the students liked music best?
   A. $\frac{1}{10}$ B. $\frac{1}{4}$ C. $\frac{3}{20}$ D. $\frac{3}{10}$

2. What fraction of the students liked sports best?
   A. $\frac{1}{5}$ B. $\frac{1}{10}$ C. $\frac{1}{4}$ D. $\frac{3}{20}$

3. What fraction of the students did not like sports best?
   A. $\frac{7}{20}$ B. $\frac{11}{20}$ C. $\frac{17}{20}$ D. $\frac{2}{5}$

The scores for a 15-point test are shown at the right. Make a frequency table.

```
15  13  12  14  12  14
14  12  10   9  10  12
14   9  10  12   8  11
12  10   9  12  10  12
```

4. What is the frequency of the score that appeared the most often?
   A. 9   B. 6   C. 7   D. 8

5. If 9 is the lowest passing score, how many scores are passing scores?
   A. 23   B. 1   C. 24   D. 22

6. Name the scale of the number line.
   A. 9–13   B. 4–9   C. 9–29   D. 29–38

   9 13 17 21 25 29

7. Name the interval of the number line.
   A. 4   B. 3   C. 5   D. 2

8. Find the range of 10, 29, 13, 9, 21, 17, and 25.
   A. 4   B. 20   C. 38   D. 9

Use the line plot to answer Exercises 9 -10.

9. Name the outlier in the line plot.
   A. 0   B. 9   C. 6   D. 12

10. Name the cluster in the line plot.
    A. between 0 and 12   B. between 0 and 6
    C. between 3 and 6   D. between 6 and 12

    0   3   6   9   12

11. Find the mode(s) of 13, 15, 13, 19, 18, 16, and 15.
    A. 13, 15   B. 13   C. 15   D. 16

12. Find the median of 13, 15, 13, 19, 18, 15, and 20.
    A. 15   B. 13   C. 14.5   D. 15.5

13. Find the mean of 43, 36, 43, 37, and 41.
    A. 41   B. 43   C. 40   D. 42

1. _____
2. _____
3. _____
4. _____
5. _____
6. _____
7. _____
8. _____
9. _____
10. _____
11. _____
12. _____
13. _____

Glencoe Division, Macmillan/McGraw-Hill

Chapter 3 Test, Form 1B (continued)

14. Which digit in the numbers 59, 69, 67, 66, 74, 78, 79, 83, and 88 would *not* appear as a *stem* when drawing a stem-and-leaf plot?

   A. 5 **B.** 8 **C.** 7 **D.** 9

14. _____

The stem-and-leaf plot at the right shows the scores on a mathematics test.

5	08
6	358
7	5667
8	3555
9	69

15. Name the highest score on the test.
   A. 100 **B.** 98 **C.** 99 **D.** 85

15. _____

16. Name the score that appears the most.
   A. 85 **B.** 76 **C.** 67 **D.** 58

16. _____

A T-shirt factory conducted a color survey. Fifty-three people were asked, "What is your favorite T-shirt color?" The results are shown in the bar graph.

T-Shirt Color Survey

17. If you were the buyer for the factory, which two colors would you buy?
   A. red, white **B.** blue, red
   C. white, green **D.** white, blue

17. _____

18. Which of these five colors is the least popular?
   A. white **B.** red **C.** blue **D.** yellow

18. _____

Salaries at The Economy Company are shown in the frequency table at the right.

The Economy Company

Salary	Number of Employees
$12,000	2
$18,000	6
$24,000	5
$28,000	2
$58,000	1
$76,000	1

19. Which number would you use to attract new employees?
   A. mean **B.** mode
   C. median or mode **D.** median

19. _____

20. What is that average salary to the nearest thousand dollars?
   A. $18,000 **B.** $26,000 **C.** $24,000 **D.** $30,000

20. _____

BONUS Julio's test scores in global studies for the semester are 68, 85, 78, 74, 79, 93, 88, and 75. He has one more test to take for the semester.

If he needs a mean score of 80 to receive a B−, what must he score on the last test?
   A. 80 **B.** 78 **C.** 90 **D.** not possible

_____

If he needs a mean score of 90 to receive an A−, what must he score on the last test?
   A. 90 **B.** 100 **C.** 95 **D.** not possible

_____

Chapter 3 Test

Form 2A

Use the frequency table for Exercises 1-2.

Grade 7 Students

Weight (kg)	Tally
40	III
45	HHT I
50	HHT HHT
55	III
60	III
65	I

1. How many students were 50 kilograms or more?
2. What is true about the mean, median, and mode?

Find the range for each set of data.

3. 16, 8, 23, 19, 11, 20, 5, 29, 33
4. 8.6, 9.1, 10.0, 4.5, 7.9, 11.7, 2.0
5. Rita's grades on five Spanish tests were 96, 84, 79, 81, and 70. Find an appropriate scale and interval. Draw a number line to show them.

Make a line plot for each set of data. Circle any outliers.

6. 45, 70, 62, 65, 66, 62   7. 3, 6, 7, 6, 4, 5, 6, 4

Find the mode(s), median, and mean for each set of data.

8. 6, 11, 40, 11, 5, 2, 9, 12, 12
9. 60, 68, 64, 60, 63, 60, 67, 73, 58, 60, 49
10. 1.4, 1.2, 1.0, 1.0, 1.6, 0.8, 1.6, 1.2, 1.0

11. Make a stem-and-leaf plot for the set of data:
96, 109, 77, 76, 85, 83, 93, 106

Larry Bird scored 27, 33, 18, 32, 35, 22, 31, 39, 28, and 26 points in ten games.

12. Make a stem-and-leaf plot of these data.
13. About how many points might you expect Larry Bird to score in a game?

The graph at the right shows the men's shirt sales for the month of March.

Men's Shirt Sales for March

14. Which were the two most popular neck sizes?
15. Which number would be the most useful in deciding which sizes to order when the new styles come out: mean, median, or mode?

BONUS In your own words, describe the mean. Then explain how it is different from the median.

1. _____
2. _____
3. _____
4. _____
5. _____
6. _____
7. _____
8. _____
9. _____
10. _____
11. _____
12. _____
13. _____
14. _____
15. _____

_____

Chapter 3 Test

Form 2B _____

Scores on a ten-question quiz are shown at the right.

Reading Quiz	
Score	Tally
2	II
3	IIII
4	I
5	IIII
6	II
7	HIT II
8	III
9	III
10	I

1. How many students scored better than 6?

2. How many students scored below the mode and the median?

Find the range for each set of data.

3. 105, 116, 125, 131, 79, 79, 106, 116

4. 2.4, 2.3, 2.9, 2.4, 2.3, 3.1, 2.4, 2.7

5. Sonja's golf scores for five rounds were 88, 83, 87, 80, and 90. Find an appropriate scale and interval. Draw a number line to show them.

Make a line plot for each set of data. Circle any outliers.

6. 0, 2, 1, 0, 2, 3, 2, 1, 3, 4, 3, 4, 7

7. 15, 20, 20, 17, 17, 19, 18, 19, 18, 19, 18, 17

Find the mode(s), median, and mean for each set of data.

8. 23, 22, 22, 24, 23, 19, 25, 21, 20

9. 7.8, 9.3, 8.8, 8.4, 9.0, 6.7, 8.2, 5.6, 8.6

10. 414, 387, 455, 508, 432, 545, 387, 431, 527

Make a stem-and-leaf plot for each set of data in Exercises 11 and 12.

11. 30, 41, 27, 18, 22, 19, 37, 22, 26

12. 5, 12, 17, 20, 26, 29, 35, 35, 3, 12, 17, 20, 26, 29, 35

13. At Prep Textiles, 6 employees earn $20,000, 3 earn $32,000, and 2 earn $62,500. List the salaries in a frequency table.

14. Find the mean, median, and mode of the salaries.

15. Which number(s) would you use to best describe the salaries: mean, median, or mode? Explain.

BONUS Make up a set of data with at least 9 items that have the same number for the mean, median, and mode.

1. _____

2. _____

3. _____

4. _____

5. _____

6. _____

7. _____

8. _____

9. _____

10. _____

11. _____

12. _____

13. _____

14. _____

15. _____

Chapter 3 Quiz A

Use with Lessons 3-1 through 3-4 ■■■■■■■■■

Josh showed in a circle graph how he budgets his money.

Josh's Budget

recreation

$7

$5 savings

clothing $13

lunches $10

$5

miscellaneous

1. What fraction of the budget is spent on savings?
2. How much more money is spent on clothing and lunches than on recreation and miscellaneous?
3. How much more money is spent on recreation and savings than on lunches?

Make a frequency table.

4. Which temperature appeared the most often?
5. Which temperature appeared least?

Sea City Temperatures (in degrees Fahrenheit)				
40	40	20	30	10
40	20	20	30	30
30	20	10	30	40

Find the range for each set of data.

6. 28, 78, 53, 37, 59
7. 12, 17, 2, 0, 11, 6, 21, 18
8. 4.9, 6.1, 6.5, 8.8, 5.5, 3.3, 5.5, 7.3, 8.1

Make a line plot for each set of data.

9. 5, 7, 6, 7, 4, 6, 5, 7, 6
10. 25, 15, 20, 20, 10, 15, 25

1. _____
2. _____
3. _____
4. _____
5. _____
6. _____
7. _____
8. _____
9. _____
10. _____

Chapter 3 Quiz B

Use with Lessons 3-5 through 3-8 ■■■■■■■■■

Find the mode(s), median, and mean for each set of data.

1. 4, 5, 8, 7, 6, 8, 9
2. 88, 89, 92, 90, 88, 92, 93
3. 12.9, 12.0, 13.0, 13.1, 13.3
4. 755, 780, 755, 805, 805
5. 2.92, 3.04, 2.94, 2.93, 2.91, 2.94, 2.94, 2.91, 2.93

Sixty students were asked who they would choose for class secretary. The graph at the right shows the results.

Election for Secretary

Number
40
30
20
10

Sam   Zoe   Maria

6. Who is most likely to win?
7. Who is least likely to win?
8. If Maria gives Sam her votes, will he win?

Make a stem-and-leaf plot for each set of data.

9. 40, 48, 44, 40, 43, 40, 47, 53, 38, 40
10. 123, 132, 136, 145, 135, 156, 141, 135, 129, 155

1. _____
2. _____
3. _____
4. _____
5. _____
6. _____
7. _____
8. _____
9. _____
10. _____

Cumulative Review Chapters 1-3

Evaluate each expression. (Lesson 1-7)

1. $48 \div 3 + 5 \cdot 7$

2. $4(11 - 6) \div 2 + 8$

Evaluate each expression if a = 7, b = 9, and c = 3. (Lesson 1-8)

3. $2a - b$

4. $3(b - c) + 6$

5. Write 8^4 as a product. (Lesson 1-9)

6. Write $6 \cdot 6 \cdot 6 \cdot 6 \cdot 6$ using exponents. (Lesson 1-9)

Solve each equation. (Lesson 1-10)

7. $x + 35 = 71$

8. $12y = 120$

9. Order 20.006, 2.273, 20.44, and 20.4 from least to greatest. (Lesson 2-1)

Estimate. Use an appropriate strategy. (Lesson 2-3)

10. $29.64 - 15.19$

11. 21.99×38.75

Multiply or divide. (Lessons 2-4, 2-7)

12. $0.016 \overline{)\,2.56}$

13. 0.00703×10^7

Change from standard form to scientific notation or vice versa. (Lesson 2-6)

14. 1.05×10^5

15. $127,000,000$

16. Divide $0.07 \overline{)\,0.00321}$. Round to the nearest hundredth. (Lesson 2-8)

17. Complete 8,195 g = ■ kg. (Lesson 2-9)

18. Make a line plot for the data 13, 15, 14, 15, 17, 12, 14, 13, 17, 16, and 14 (Lesson 3-4)

Find the following for the data in Exercise 18. (Lessons 3-3, 3-5)

19. range   20. mode(s)   21. median   22. mean

23. Make a stem-and-leaf plot for the data 54, 66, 32, 24, 27, 43, 36, 49, 51, 32, and 38. (Lesson 3-6)

On the day before class elections, 55 students were asked who they would choose for the class president. The graph at the right shows the results. (Lesson 3-7)

Election for President

24. Who do you think will win the election?

25. Who is most likely to lose?

1. _____
2. _____
3. _____
4. _____
5. _____
6 _____
7 _____
8 _____
9. _____
10. _____
11. _____
12. _____
13. _____
14. _____
15. _____
16. _____
17. _____
18. _____
19. _____
20. _____
21. _____
22. _____
23. _____
24. _____
25. _____

Cumulative Test Chapters 1-3

Evaluate.

1. $3(15 - 9) \div 6 + 3$ **A.** 6   **B.** 2   **C.** 3   **D.** 9

Evaluate each expression if *a* = 8, *b* = 3, and *c* = 7.

2. $b + 2a$ **A.** 48   **B.** 40   **C.** 19   **D.** 29

3. $7 + (2c - a)$ **A.** 9   **B.** 13   **C.** 10   **D.** 14

4. Write 6^3 as a product.

   A. $6 \cdot 6 \cdot 6$ **B.** $3 \cdot 3 \cdot 3 \cdot 3$ **C.** $6 \cdot 6 \cdot 6 \cdot 6$ **D.** $3 \cdot 3 \cdot 3 \cdot 3 \cdot 3 \cdot 3$

5. Write $5 \cdot 5 \cdot 5 \cdot 5$ using exponents.

   A. 4^5 **B.** 5^6 **C.** 4^6 **D.** 5^4

6. Solve $s \div 9 = 16$.   **A.** 7   **B.** 1.7   **C.** 144   **D.** 25

Estimate. Use an appropriate strategy.

7. $19.75 + 32.18$ **A.** 50   **B.** 60   **C.** 55   **D.** 59

8. $2.8)\overline{0.91}$ **A.** 0.03   **B.** 0.3   **C.** 3   **D.** 0.003

Multiply or divide.

9. $0.018)\overline{0.324}$ **A.** 20   **B.** 1.8   **C.** 18   **D.** 0.2

10. $10^6 \times 0.000029$ **A.** 2.9   **B.** 290   **C.** 0.29   **D.** 29

Change from standard form to scientific notation or vice versa.

11. 110,000,000   **A.** 1×10^9 **B.** 1.1×10^7 **C.** 1×10^8 **D.** 1.1×10^8

12. 7.1×10^3 **A.** 71   **B.** 710   **C.** 7,100   **D.** 71,000

13. Divide $0.04)\overline{0.00935}$. Round to the nearest hundredth.

   A. 0.23   **B.** 2.2   **C.** 0.023   **D.** 0.22

14. $1.2 \text{ kL} = \blacksquare \text{ L}$ **A.** 1,200   **B.** 120   **C.** 0.12   **D.** 1.2

15. Which digit would *not* appear as a *leaf* in a stem-and-leaf plot of the data: 79, 88, 87, 85, 84, 74, 84, 86, and 89?

   A. 8   **B.** 3   **C.** 9   **D.** 5

Find the following numbers for the data in Exercise 15.

16. mode(s)   **A.** 80   **B.** 85   **C.** 84   **D.** 16

17. median   **A.** 16   **B.** 85   **C.** 84   **D.** 83

18. mean   **A.** 85   **B.** 90   **C.** 84   **D.** 16

Use the line plot to answer Exercises 19 and 20.

19. Name the outlier.   **A.** 80   **B.** 40   **C.** 60   **D.** 0

20. Name the cluster.

   A. between 0 and 40   **B.** between 0 and 80

   C. between 40 and 80   **D.** between 0 and 60

1. _____
2. _____
3. _____
4. _____
5. _____
6. _____
7. _____
8. _____
9. _____
10. _____
11. _____
12. _____
13. _____
14. _____
15. _____
16. _____
17. _____
18. _____
19. _____
20. _____

Form 1A

1. Which number is a factor of 8,358?
   A. 5   **B.** 6   **C.** 10   **D.** 9

   1. ____

2. Which number is not a factor of 60,070?
   A. 5   **B.** 2   **C.** 10   **D.** 6

   2. ____

3. Find the prime factorization of 18.
   A. $2 \cdot 2 \cdot 3$ **B.** $3 \cdot 6$ **C.** $2 \cdot 3 \cdot 3$ **D.** $3 \cdot 3 \cdot 3$

   3. ____

4. Find the prime factorization of 42.
   A. $2 \cdot 3 \cdot 7$ **B.** $3 \cdot 3 \cdot 7$ **C.** $3 \cdot 14$ **D.** $2 \cdot 5 \cdot 5$

   4. ____

5. Find the prime factorization of 81.
   A. $3 \cdot 3 \cdot 3$ **B.** $3 \cdot 5 \cdot 7$ **C.** $3 \cdot 3 \cdot 3 \cdot 3$ **D.** $3 \cdot 3 \cdot 9$

   5. ____

6. Find the next term in the sequence 72, 66, 60, 54, . . .
   A. 52   **B.** 48   **C.** 50   **D.** 58

   6. ____

7. Find the sixth term in the sequence $16, 4, 1, \frac{1}{4}, \ldots$
   A. $\frac{1}{64}$ **B.** $\frac{1}{16}$ **C.** $\frac{1}{32}$ **D.** $\frac{1}{12}$

   7. ____

8. Find the GCF of 48 and 56.
   A. 336   **B.** 4   **C.** 8   **D.** 9

   8. ____

9. Find the GCF of 8, 20, and 36.
   A. 2   **B.** 4   **C.** 6   **D.** 8

   9. ____

10. Express $\frac{36}{60}$ in simplest form.
    A. $\frac{9}{15}$ **B.** $\frac{18}{30}$ **C.** $\frac{12}{20}$ **D.** $\frac{3}{5}$

    10. ____

11. Express $\frac{99}{81}$ in simplest form.
    A. $\frac{11}{9}$ **B.** $\frac{33}{27}$ **C.** $\frac{11}{10}$ **D.** $\frac{27}{33}$

    11. ____

12. Express $\frac{32}{72}$ in simplest form.
    A. $\frac{16}{36}$ **B.** $\frac{8}{18}$ **C.** $\frac{4}{9}$ **D.** $\frac{18}{8}$

    12. ____

13. Express $\frac{13}{20}$ as a decimal.
    A. 6.5   **B.** 0.35   **C.** 0.65   **D.** 0.56

    13. ____

14. Express 0.125 as a fraction in simplest form.
    A. $\frac{1}{8}$ **B.** $\frac{1}{6}$ **C.** $\frac{3}{8}$ **D.** $\frac{1}{5}$

    14. ____

Chapter 4 Test Form 1A (continued)

15. Express $\frac{11}{12}$ as a decimal.

    A. 0.92   **B.** 0.916   **C.** 0.9166   **D.** $0.91\overline{6}$

15. _____

A bag contains 4 blue, 5 red, 1 green, and 2 white marbles. If you draw a marble at random:

16. What is the probability of drawing a blue marble?

    A. $\frac{5}{12}$ **B.** $\frac{1}{4}$ **C.** $\frac{1}{12}$ **D.** $\frac{1}{3}$

16. _____

17. What is the probability of drawing a marble that is not red?

    A. $\frac{7}{12}$ **B.** $\frac{5}{12}$ **C.** $\frac{1}{4}$ **D.** $\frac{1}{3}$

17. _____

18. Find the LCM of 12 and 16.

    A. 24   **B.** 192   **C.** 48   **D.** 96

18. _____

19. Find the LCM of 10, 12, and 18.

    A. 2   **B.** 18   **C.** 2,160   **D.** 180

19. _____

Replace each ● to make a true statement.

20. $\frac{6}{7}$ ● $\frac{3}{5}$

    A. >   **B.** <   **C.** =   **D.** +

20. _____

21. $\frac{3}{2}$ ● $\frac{4}{3}$

    A. >   **B.** <   **C.** =   **D.** ×

21. _____

22. $\frac{7}{12}$ ● $\frac{5}{8}$

    A. >   **B.** <   **C.** =   **D.** –

22. _____

23. In the Fibonacci sequence, 1 is a perfect cube. What is the only other perfect cube in the first twelve terms?

    A. 27   **B.** 64   **C.** 8   **D.** 2,197

23. _____

24. The sixth Fibonacci number is:

    A. 2   **B.** 5   **C.** 13   **D.** 8

24. _____

25. Carlos plans to open a savings account with $100 from his March paycheck and then increase the amount he deposits by $100 each month. How many months will it take for Carlos to have $600 in deposits in his account?

    A. July   **B.** 3   **C.** 4   **D.** 6

25. _____

BONUS Find the next two terms of the sequence 65, 62, 57, 50, 41, 30, . . .

    A. 17, 2   **B.** 19, 4   **C.** 16, 1   **D.** 16, 3

_____

Form 1B _____ *Chapter 4 Test*

1. Which number is a factor of 2,196?
   A. 9   **B.** 10   **C.** 5   **D.** 7

   1. ____

2. Which number is not a factor of 1,296?
   A. 2   **B.** 6   **C.** 9   **D.** 5

   2. ____

3. Find the prime factorization of 70.
   A. $2 \cdot 35$ **B.** $2 \cdot 5 \cdot 7$ **C.** $3 \cdot 3 \cdot 7$ **D.** $2 \cdot 2 \cdot 5 \cdot 7$

   3. ____

4. Find the prime factorization of 182.
   A. $2 \cdot 91$ **B.** $14 \cdot 17$ **C.** $2 \cdot 7 \cdot 13$ **D.** $13 \cdot 14$

   4. ____

5. Find the prime factorization of 550.
   A. $3 \cdot 5 \cdot 19$ **B.** $2 \cdot 7 \cdot 17$ **C.** $5 \cdot 110$ **D.** $2 \cdot 5 \cdot 5 \cdot 11$

   5. ____

6. Find the next term in the sequence 11, 12.7, 14.4, 16.1, . . .
   A. 17.8   **B.** 14.4   **C.** 17.2   **D.** 18.1

   6. ____

7. Find the sixth term in the sequence 1, 4, 9, 16, 25, . . .
   A. 30   **B.** 36   **C.** 49   **D.** 35

   7. ____

8. Find the GCF of 18 and 54.
   A. 6   **B.** 9   **C.** 18   **D.** 12

   8. ____

9. Find the GCF of 16, 56, and 64.
   A. 8   **B.** 16   **C.** 4   **D.** 2

   9. ____

10. Express $\frac{12}{27}$ in simplest form.
    A. $\frac{1}{3}$ **B.** $\frac{1}{2}$ **C.** $\frac{4}{9}$ **D.** $\frac{3}{7}$

    10. ____

11. Express $\frac{63}{36}$ in simplest form.
    A. $\frac{4}{7}$ **B.** $\frac{7}{4}$ **C.** $\frac{21}{12}$ **D.** $\frac{12}{21}$

    11. ____

12. Express $\frac{72}{81}$ in simplest form.
    A. $\frac{24}{27}$ **B.** $\frac{7}{8}$ **C.** $\frac{8}{7}$ **D.** $\frac{8}{9}$

    12. ____

13. Express $\frac{24}{200}$ as a decimal.
    A. 0.24   **B.** 1.2   **C.** 0.12   **D.** 0.024

    13. ____

14. Express 2.75 as a fraction in simplest form.
    A. $\frac{11}{4}$ **B.** $\frac{9}{4}$ **C.** $\frac{5}{2}$ **D.** $\frac{2}{5}$

    14. ____

Chapter 4 Test Form 1B (continued)

15. Express $\frac{5}{11}$ as a decimal.   15. _____

    A. 0.45 **B.** $0.\overline{45}$ **C.** 0.46 **D.** $0.4\overline{5}$

A bag contains 2 blue, 3 red, 4 green, and 6 white marbles. If you draw a marble at random:

16. What is the probability of drawing a white marble?   16. _____

    A. $\frac{1}{5}$ **B.** $\frac{4}{15}$ **C.** $\frac{2}{5}$ **D.** $\frac{3}{5}$

17. What is the probability of drawing a red or green marble?   17. _____

    A. $\frac{1}{3}$ **B.** $\frac{1}{15}$ **C.** $\frac{7}{15}$ **D.** $\frac{8}{15}$

18. Find the LCM of 14 and 49.   18. _____

    A. 96   **B.** 686   **C.** 49   **D.** 98

19. Find the LCM of 15, 25, and 125.   19. _____

    A. 375   **B.** 125   **C.** 5   **D.** 46,875

Replace each ● to make a true statement.

20. $\frac{2}{3}$ ● $\frac{4}{5}$ 20. _____

    A. $>$ **B.** $<$ **C.** $=$ **D.** $+$

21. $\frac{7}{8}$ ● $\frac{13}{16}$ 21. _____

    A. $>$ **B.** $<$ **C.** $=$ **D.** $\times$

22. $\frac{5}{9}$ ● $\frac{7}{12}$ 22. _____

    A. $>$ **B.** $<$ **C.** $=$ **D.** $\div$

23. Find the sixth term in the sequence 4, 8, 12, 16, . . .   23. _____

    A. 26   **B.** 24   **C.** 23   **D.** 25

24. Carol spends 4 hours every day watching television. Find   24. _____
the fraction of the day he spends watching television.

    A. $\frac{5}{6}$ **B.** $\frac{1}{2}$ **C.** $\frac{1}{6}$ **D.** $\frac{1}{4}$

25. In the Fibonacci sequence 1, 1, 2, 3, 5, . . . , what is the least   25. _____
common multiple of the sixth term and the twelfth term.

    A. 144   **B.** 8   **C.** 1,152   **D.** 18

BONUS Find the seventh term of the sequence 2, 3, 5, 9, 17, . . .   _____

    A. 60   **B.** 65   **C.** 58   **D.** 62

Form 2A

Determine whether each number is divisible by 2, 3, 4, 5, 6, 9, or 10.

1. 324   2. 1,980

Write the prime factorization of each number.

3. 51   4. 98   5. 72

Identify each sequence as arithmetic, geometric, or neither. Then find the next three terms in the sequence.

6. 3, 9, 27, 81, . . .   7. 1, 7, 13, 19, . . .

Find the GCF of each set of numbers.

8. 48, 56   9. 72, 84, 132

Write each fraction in simplest form.

10. $\frac{4}{18}$ 11. $\frac{30}{35}$ 12. $\frac{28}{48}$

Express each fraction as a decimal and each decimal as a fraction in simplest form. Use bar notation if necessary.

13. $\frac{7}{8}$ 14. 0.28   15. $\frac{7}{11}$

The spinner shown at the right is equally likely to stop on each of the regions. Find the probability that the spinner will stop on

16. a composite number.

17. a factor of 15.

Find the LCM of each set of numbers.

18. 24, 36   19. 24, 30, 360

Replace each ● with a $<$, $>$, or $=$ to make a true statement.

20. $\frac{7}{8}$ ● $\frac{8}{10}$ 21. $\frac{10}{15}$ ● $\frac{8}{14}$

22. A condominium rents for $800 a month. The monthly rent is expected to increase $25 each year. How much will the monthly rent be at the end of 4 years?

23. In a school election, 75 of the 125 seventh-graders actually voted, and 85 of the 100 eighth-graders actually voted. Which grade had the better voter turnout?

24. What is true about every third Fibonacci number, if the Fibonacci sequence is 1, 1, 2, 3, 5, 8, 13, . . . ?

25. What is the only perfect square other than 1 in the first twelve terms of the Fibonacci sequence?

BONUS I am a fraction less than one and in simplest form. My numerator and denominator are both prime numbers greater than 13 and less than 23. Name me.

1._____

2._____

3._____

4._____

5._____

6._____

7._____

8._____

9._____

10._____

11._____

12._____

13._____

14._____

15._____

16._____

17._____

18._____

19._____

20._____

21._____

22._____

23._____

24._____

25._____

_____

Form 2B _____

Determine whether each number is divisible by 2, 3, 4, 5, 6, 9, or 10.

1. 360　　　　　2. 480

Write the prime factorization of each number.

3. 130　　　　4. 378　　　　5. 102

Identify each sequence as arithmetic, geometric, or neither. Then find the next three terms in the sequence.

6. $2, 1, \frac{1}{2}, \frac{1}{4}, \ldots$　　　7. $1, 2, 4, 7, 11, \ldots$

Find the GCF of each set of numbers.

8. 30, 54　　　　9. 20, 36, 48

Write each fraction in simplest form.

10. $\frac{14}{24}$　　　11. $\frac{32}{36}$　　　12. $\frac{39}{52}$

Express each fraction as a decimal and each decimal as a fraction in simplest form. Use bar notation if necessary.

13. $\frac{8}{9}$　　　14. 0.58　　　15. $\frac{5}{8}$

The spinner shown at the right is equally likely to stop on each of the regions. Find the probability that the spinner will stop on

16. an odd number.

17. a factor of 24.

Find the LCM of each set of numbers.

18. 14, 49　　　19. 12, 24, 36

Replace each ● with a <, >, or = to make a true statement.

20. $\frac{2}{3}$ ● $\frac{3}{5}$　　　21. $\frac{5}{6}$ ● $\frac{14}{16}$

22. Ellie scored 23 out of 25 on a health test. Cheryl scored 47 out of 50 on her test. Who scored higher?

23. Jeff's math average dropped one half of a point each week for 10 consecutive weeks. If his average was 80 originally, what was his average at the end of 9 weeks?

24. If the Fibonacci numbers, 1, 1, 2, 3, 5, 8, . . . are squared and then adjacent squares are added together, a new sequence is formed. What are the first five numbers in the sequence?

25. Find the greatest common factor of the fifth and tenth terms of the Fibonacci sequence.

BONUS Find the two smallest numbers whose GCF is 9 and whose LCM is 54.

1._____
2._____
3._____
4._____
5._____
6._____
7._____
8._____
9._____
10._____
11._____
12._____
13._____
14._____
15._____
16._____
17._____
18._____
19._____
20._____
21._____
22._____
23._____
24._____
25._____
_____

Glencoe Division, Macmillan/McGraw-Hill

Use with Lessons 4-1 through 4-5 ═══════════

Determine whether each number is divisible by 2, 3, 4, 5, 6, 9, or 10.

1. 720　　　　　　**2.** 5,400

Write the prime factorization of each number.

3. 28　　　　　**4.** 64　　　　　**5.** 144

Identify each sequence as arithmetic, geometric, or neither. Then find the next three terms in the sequence.

6. 1, 7, 13, 19, . . .　　**7.** 2, 4, 8, 14, . . .

Find the GCF of each set of numbers.

8. 28, 42　　　　**9.** 16, 36, 44

10. Find the sum of the first eight numbers in the Fibonacci sequence. What is the greatest common factor of this sum and the tenth term?

1._____

2._____

3._____

4._____

5._____

6._____

7._____

8._____

9._____

10._____

Use with Lessons 4-6 through 4-10 ═══════════

Write each fraction in simplest form.

1. $\frac{12}{64}$　　　　　**2.** $\frac{36}{30}$

3. Express $\frac{21}{25}$ as a decimal.

4. Express 0.375 as a fraction in simplest form.

The spinner shown at the right is equally likely to stop on each of the regions. Find the probability that the spinner will stop on

5. an even number.

6. a factor of 6.

Find the LCM of each set of numbers.

7. 18, 24

8. 12, 24, and 96

Replace each ● with a $<$, $>$, or $=$ to make a true statement.

9. $\frac{24}{30}$ ● $\frac{45}{50}$　　　　**10.** $\frac{14}{16}$ ● $\frac{24}{28}$

1._____

2._____

3._____

4._____

5._____

6._____

7._____

8._____

9._____

10._____

Cumulative Review Chapters 1-4

Evaluate each expression. (Lesson 1-7)

1. $6 \cdot 4 + 2 \div 2$ 2. $3(13 + 7) \div 15 + 5$

Evaluate each expression if $x = 10$, $y = 2$, and $z = 5$. (Lesson 1-8)

3. $3y + 5x$ 4. $8 + 2(x - z)$

Solve each equation. (Lesson 1-10)

5. $18c = 162$ 6. $95 = e + 66$

Estimate. Use an appropriate strategy. (Lesson 2-3)

7. 18.89×73.09 8. $87.59 - 12.73$

Multiply or divide. (Lessons 2-4, 2-7)

9. 0.000127×10^9 10. $0.00019\overline{)3.42}$

11. Divide $0.002\overline{)0.000139}$. Round to the nearest hundredth. (Lesson 2-8)

12. Write 981,000,000,000 in scientific notation. (Lesson 2-6)

13. Make a line plot for the data 45, 46, 46, 50, 46, 45 at the right. Circle any outliers. (Lesson 3-4)

Find the following for the data in Exercise 13. (Lessons 3-3, 3-5)

14. range   15. mode(s)

16. median   17. mean

18. Which score appears most often in the stem-and-leaf plot at the right? (Lesson 3-6)

| 7 | 28999 |
| 8 | 13699 |

19. Determine whether 624 is divisible by 2, 3, 4, 5, 6, 9, or 10. (Lesson 4-1)

20. Write the prime factorization for 108. (Lesson 4-2)

21. Identify the sequence 2, 9, 16, 23, . . . as arithmetic, geometric, or neither. Then find the next three terms of the sequence. (Lesson 4-3)

22. Find the ninth and tenth terms of the Fibonacci sequence. (Lesson 4-4)

23. Find the GCF and LCM of 21 and 49. (Lessons 4-5, 4-9)

24. Write $\frac{51}{68}$ in simplest form. (Lesson 4-6)

25. The spinner shown at the right is equally likely to stop on each of the regions. Find the probability that the spinner will stop on a prime number. (Lesson 4-8)

1. _____
2. _____
3. _____
4. _____
5. _____
6. _____
7. _____
8. _____
9. _____
10. _____
11. _____
12. _____
13. _____
14. _____
15. _____
16. _____
17. _____
18. _____
19. _____
20. _____
21. _____
22. _____
23. _____
24. _____
25. _____

Glencoe Division, Macmillan/McGraw-Hill

Cumulative Test Chapters 1-4

Evaluate each expression if x = 9, y = 6, and z = 2.

1. $6z - x$　　　　**A.** 21　**B.** 20　**C.** 3　**D.** 4

2. $3(x - y) - 9$　　**A.** 18　**B.** 0　**C.** 27　**D.** 9

3. Solve $a \div 7 = 14$.　**A.** 98　**B.** 2　**C.** 21　**D.** 7

4. Solve $73 = d - 28$.　**A.** 65　**B.** 55　**C.** 101　**D.** 2,044

Estimate. Use an appropriate strategy.

5. $5.3\overline{)78.89}$　　　**A.** 1.6　**B.** 17　**C.** 16　**D.** 1.7

6. $21.27 + 47.85$　　**A.** 70　**B.** 60　**C.** 80　**D.** 50

7. Divide $0.082\overline{)0.493}$. Round to the nearest hundredth.
   A. 6.012　　**B.** 6.01　　**C.** 60.1　　**D.** 6.02

8. Write 2,130,000 in scientific notation.
   A. 213×10^4　**B.** 21.3×10^5　**C.** 2.13×10^6　**D.** 2.13×10^5

Use the line plot to answer Exercises 9 through 14.

```
        x       x
        x   x   x
        x   x   x
10  13  16  19  22
                    x
```
(x's above 10, 13, 16; single x above 22)

9. Name the outlier.　**A.** 10　**B.** 16　**C.** 13　**D.** 22

10. Find the range.　**A.** 12　**B.** 16　**C.** 14.5　**D.** 22

11. Find the mode(s).　**A.** 10　**B.** 14.5　**C.** 16　**D.** 14.2

12. Find the median.　**A.** 14.2　**B.** 14　**C.** 15　**D.** 13

13. Find the mean.　**A.** 14.5　**B.** 14.09　**C.** 12　**D.** 16

14. Name the cluster.
    A. between 10 and 13　　**B.** between 10 and 16
    C. between 16 and 22　　**D.** between 13 and 22

15. Find the prime factorization of 114.
    A. $2 \cdot 3 \cdot 17$　**B.** $2 \cdot 57$　**C.** $3^2 \cdot 19$　**D.** $2 \cdot 3 \cdot 19$

16. Find the next four terms in the sequence 2, 3, 3, 4, 4, 4, ...
    A. 5, 5, 5, 5, 5　**B.** 5, 5　**C.** 5, 5, 5, 5　**D.** 5, 5, 5

17. In the Fibonacci sequence, 8 is a perfect cube. What is the only other perfect cube in the first ten terms?
    A. 27　　**B.** 64　　**C.** 1　　**D.** 125

18. Find the GCF and LCM for 12 and 24.
    A. 12; 48　**B.** 6; 24　**C.** 6; 12　**D.** 12; 24

A bag contains 5 blue, 6 red, 2 green, and 2 white marbles. If you draw a marble at random,

19. Find the probability of drawing a red marble?
    A. $\frac{3}{5}$　**B.** $\frac{1}{5}$　**C.** $\frac{2}{5}$　**D.** $\frac{4}{5}$

20. Find the probability of drawing a marble that is *not* blue?
    A. $\frac{2}{3}$　**B.** $\frac{1}{3}$　**C.** $\frac{13}{15}$　**D.** $\frac{11}{15}$

1._____
2._____
3._____
4._____
5._____
6._____
7._____
8._____
9._____
10._____
11._____
12._____
13._____
14._____
15._____
16._____
17._____
18._____
19._____
20._____

Glencoe Division, Macmillan/McGraw-Hill

Chapter 5 Test

Form 1A _____

1. Change $\frac{8}{3}$ to a mixed number.
   A. 2.6   B. $3\frac{1}{3}$ C. $2\frac{1}{3}$ D. $2\frac{2}{3}$

2. Change $3\frac{4}{5}$ to an improper fraction.
   A. $\frac{19}{5}$ B. $\frac{17}{5}$ C. $\frac{19}{4}$ D. $\frac{19}{3}$

3. Estimate $\frac{7}{8} + 3\frac{1}{16}$.
   A. 5   B. 2   C. 4   D. 3

4. Estimate $9\frac{1}{5} - 4\frac{5}{6}$.
   A. 6   B. 4   C. 5   D. 7

5. Estimate $11\frac{2}{3} \div 1\frac{4}{5}$.
   A. 11   B. 12   C. 10   D. 6

Add, subtract, multiply, or divide. Write the answer in simplest form.

6. $\frac{2}{3} + \frac{3}{8}$
   A. $\frac{5}{11}$ B. $\frac{5}{24}$ C. $\frac{1}{4}$ D. $1\frac{1}{24}$

7. $\frac{9}{11} + \frac{1}{2}$
   A. $1\frac{7}{22}$ B. $\frac{10}{13}$ C. $\frac{29}{13}$ D. $\frac{9}{22}$

8. $\frac{7}{8} - \frac{5}{6}$
   A. $\frac{1}{12}$ B. 1   C. $\frac{1}{24}$ D. $\frac{1}{7}$

9. $\frac{11}{12} \times \frac{9}{22}$
   A. $\frac{10}{17}$ B. $\frac{3}{8}$ C. $\frac{3}{4}$ D. $\frac{99}{264}$

10. $\frac{3}{5} \div \frac{7}{15}$
    A. $\frac{7}{9}$ B. $\frac{7}{25}$ C. $\frac{1}{2}$ D. $1\frac{2}{7}$

11. $2\frac{3}{4} \div \frac{7}{8}$
    A. 3   B. $\frac{7}{22}$ C. $3\frac{1}{7}$ D. $\frac{88}{28}$

12. $\frac{11}{12} - \frac{5}{8}$
    A. $\frac{3}{2}$ B. $\frac{3}{10}$ C. $\frac{7}{24}$ D. $\frac{3}{8}$

13. $\frac{3}{2} \times \frac{5}{18}$
    A. $\frac{5}{12}$ B. $\frac{2}{5}$ C. $\frac{2}{9}$ D. $\frac{5}{8}$

1. _____
2. _____
3. _____
4. _____
5. _____
6. _____
7. _____
8. _____
9. _____
10. _____
11. _____
12. _____
13. _____

Glencoe Division, Macmillan/McGraw-Hill

Chapter 5 Test Form 1A (continued)

14. Compute $6 \times 2\frac{5}{6}$ mentally.

    A. 13   **B.** 17   **C.** 18   **D.** 14

14. _____

15. Compute $\frac{3}{8} \times 8\frac{8}{9}$ mentally.

    A. 8   **B.** 9   **C.** $3\frac{1}{3}$ **D.** 6

15. _____

Add or subtract. Write the answer in simplest form.

16. $2\frac{1}{8} + 1\frac{5}{12}$

    A. $3\frac{3}{10}$ **B.** $3\frac{5}{96}$ **C.** $3\frac{1}{4}$ **D.** $3\frac{13}{24}$

16. _____

17. $10\frac{1}{6} - 4\frac{3}{14}$

    A. $5\frac{20}{21}$ **B.** $6\frac{1}{4}$ **C.** $6\frac{1}{10}$ **D.** $5\frac{1}{4}$

17. _____

18. Find the perimeter of a square with side $3\frac{3}{4}$ feet.

    A. 15 ft   **B.** 16 ft   **C.** $15\frac{1}{4}$ ft   **D.** $16\frac{1}{2}$ ft

18. _____

19. Find the circumference of a circle whose diameter is $\frac{5}{9}$ yard.

    A. 2 yd   **B.** $3\frac{31}{63}$ yd   **C.** $1\frac{47}{63}$ yd   **D.** 4 yd

19. _____

20. Find the circumference of a circle whose radius is 2.75 feet.

    A. 18.84 ft   **B.** 17.27 ft   **C.** 17 ft   **D.** 18 ft

20. _____

21. The spinner at the right tells the number of dollars you win. Find the expected value of a spin.

    A. $2.00   **B.** $2.25

    C. $3.00   **D.** $2.75

21. _____

22. In Exercise 21, over the long-term, would you expect to win, lose, or break even if each spin cost $2?

    A. win   **B.** lose   **C.** break even   **D.** none

22. _____

23. Jaime and three friends bought $\frac{3}{4}$ pound of trail mix. If they split the mix equally, how much will each person get?

    A. $\frac{1}{16}$ lb   **B.** $\frac{3}{8}$ lb   **C.** $\frac{3}{16}$ lb   **D.** $\frac{2}{5}$ lb

23. _____

24. A taxi charges $1.20 for the first $\frac{1}{5}$ mile and 50¢ for each additional $\frac{1}{5}$ mile. What is the best estimate for the cost of a 5-mile taxi ride?

    A. $13   **B.** $11   **C.** $15   **D.** $10

24. _____

25. Rosa bought a container of peanuts. She gave $\frac{1}{4}$ of it to one sister, $\frac{1}{3}$ to another, $\frac{1}{6}$ to her brother, and kept the rest for herself. How much did she keep?

    A. $\frac{1}{2}$ **B.** $\frac{1}{8}$ **C.** $\frac{3}{4}$ **D.** $\frac{1}{4}$

25. _____

BONUS Solve $\frac{1}{4} + \frac{5}{24} = x - \frac{3}{8}$.

    A. $\frac{5}{6}$ **B.** $\frac{1}{12}$ **C.** $\frac{5}{8}$ **D.** $\frac{6}{7}$

_____

Form 1B

Chapter 5 Test

1. Change $\frac{10}{7}$ to a mixed number.   1. _____
   A. $1\frac{3}{7}$ B. $2\frac{1}{7}$ C. $1\frac{1}{7}$ D. $2\frac{3}{7}$

2. Change $2\frac{3}{16}$ to an improper fraction.   2. _____
   A. $\frac{22}{16}$ B. $\frac{11}{8}$ C. $\frac{35}{16}$ D. $\frac{45}{16}$

3. Estimate $\frac{2}{5} + 5\frac{1}{2}$.   3. _____
   A. 5   B. 6   C. 7   D. 8

4. Estimate $8\frac{13}{16} - 5\frac{1}{3}$.   4. _____
   A. 3   B. 4   C. 5   D. 2

5. Estimate $12\frac{2}{5} \div 3\frac{1}{8}$.   5. _____
   A. 4   B. 3   C. 5   D. 2

Add, subtract, multiply, or divide. Write the answer in simplest form.

6. $\frac{4}{5} + \frac{5}{6}$ 6. _____
   A. $\frac{48}{30}$ B. $1\frac{19}{30}$ C. $\frac{9}{11}$ D. $1\frac{2}{3}$

7. $\frac{1}{6} + \frac{7}{9}$ 7. _____
   A. $\frac{7}{15}$ B. $\frac{8}{15}$ C. $1\frac{1}{18}$ D. $\frac{17}{18}$

8. $\frac{6}{7} - \frac{3}{4}$ 8. _____
   A. 1   B. $\frac{3}{11}$ C. $\frac{8}{7}$ D. $\frac{3}{28}$

9. $\frac{10}{13} \times \frac{26}{5}$ 9. _____
   A. 4   B. 2   C. $\frac{260}{65}$ D. 1

10. $\frac{3}{8} \div \frac{3}{4}$ 10. _____
    A. 2   B. $\frac{9}{32}$ C. $\frac{1}{2}$ D. $\frac{1}{32}$

11. $2\frac{1}{2} \div 4\frac{3}{4}$ 11. _____
    A. $1\frac{9}{10}$ B. $\frac{3}{5}$ C. $\frac{10}{19}$ D. $\frac{95}{8}$

12. $\frac{7}{8} - \frac{5}{12}$ 12. _____
    A. $\frac{1}{10}$ B. $\frac{11}{24}$ C. $\frac{1}{2}$ D. $2\frac{1}{12}$

13. $1\frac{1}{2} \times 4\frac{1}{3}$ 13. _____
    A. $6\frac{1}{2}$ B. $\frac{3}{13}$ C. 6   D. $\frac{16}{5}$

Glencoe Division, Macmillan/McGraw-Hill

Chapter 5 Test, Form 1B (continued)

14. Compute $4 \times 3\frac{3}{4}$ mentally.   **14.** _____
     A. 13   **B.** $14\frac{1}{4}$ **C.** $13\frac{3}{4}$ **D.** 15

15. Compute $\frac{3}{5} \times 5\frac{5}{8}$ mentally.   **15.** _____
     A. $3\frac{3}{8}$ **B.** $5\frac{1}{8}$ **C.** $6\frac{3}{8}$ **D.** $3\frac{1}{8}$

Add or subtract. Write the answer in simplest form.

16. $3\frac{5}{9} + 2\frac{6}{7}$ **16.** _____
     A. $5\frac{19}{63}$ **B.** $6\frac{19}{63}$ **C.** $6\frac{26}{63}$ **D.** $5\frac{11}{16}$

17. $9\frac{2}{3} - 7\frac{5}{6}$.   **17.** _____
     A. $2\frac{1}{6}$ **B.** $1\frac{1}{6}$ **C.** $1\frac{5}{6}$ **D.** $2\frac{5}{6}$

18. Find the perimeter of a square with side $1\frac{9}{16}$ inches.   **18.** _____
     A. $6\frac{1}{4}$ in.   **B.** $4\frac{9}{16}$ in.   **C.** 5 in.   **D.** $5\frac{1}{4}$ in.

19. Find the circumference of a circle whose diameter is 3.5 yards.   **19.** _____
     A. 10.99 yd   **B.** 5.495 yd   **C.** 11 yd   **D.** 5 yd

20. Find the circumference of a circle whose radius is $2\frac{1}{4}$ feet.   **20.** _____
     A. $14\frac{1}{2}$ ft   **B.** $13\frac{3}{7}$ ft   **C.** $14\frac{1}{7}$ ft   **D.** $13\frac{1}{7}$ ft

21. The spinner at the right tells the number of dollars you win. Find the expected value of a spin.   **21.** _____
     A. \$2.00   **B.** \$2.75
     C. \$3.00   **D.** \$1.75

22. In Exercise 21, over the long-term, would you expect to win, lose, or break even if each spin cost \$1.75?   **22.** _____
     A. win   **B.** lose   **C.** break even   **D.** none

23. Raman sold 15 quarter-page ads for the school magazine. How many pages of ads did he sell?   **23.** _____
     A. $4\frac{1}{4}$ **B.** $3\frac{3}{4}$ **C.** 3   **D.** $2\frac{3}{4}$

24. Rina walked $4\frac{3}{4}$ miles, and Sara walked $5\frac{1}{2}$ miles. How much farther did Sara walk than Rina?   **24.** _____
     A. $\frac{5}{8}$ mi   **B.** $\frac{3}{4}$ mi   **C.** $\frac{7}{8}$ mi   **D.** $\frac{1}{4}$ mi

25. Usually Emory rides his bicycle $5\frac{4}{5}$ miles a day. Today he didn't have much time, so he rode half his usual distance. How far did he ride?   **25.** _____
     A. $2\frac{7}{10}$ **B.** $3\frac{4}{10}$ **C.** $2\frac{4}{10}$ **D.** $2\frac{9}{10}$

BONUS If each side of a STOP sign measures about $12\frac{13}{16}$ inches, what is its perimeter to the nearest foot?   _____
     A. 7 ft   **B.** 6 ft   **C.** 10 ft   **D.** 9 ft

Form 2A

Change each improper fraction to a mixed number or vice versa.

1. $\frac{9}{4}$

2. $4\frac{6}{7}$

3. $\frac{28}{6}$

Estimate.

4. $\frac{8}{9} + 2\frac{1}{4}$

5. $10\frac{7}{8} - 6\frac{1}{5}$

6. $12\frac{2}{9} \div 1\frac{4}{5}$

Compute mentally.

7. $4 \times 5\frac{1}{2}$

8. $2\frac{1}{3} \times 9$

9. $\frac{5}{6} \times 12\frac{3}{5}$

Add, subtract, multiply, or divide. Write each answer in simplest form.

10. $\frac{2}{5} + \frac{5}{8}$

11. $\frac{11}{13} + \frac{2}{3}$

12. $\frac{4}{5} - \frac{8}{15}$

13. $\frac{7}{12} \times \frac{3}{14}$

14. $\frac{3}{7} \div \frac{5}{14}$

15. $1\frac{3}{5} \div \frac{7}{15}$

16. $4\frac{1}{3} + 2\frac{1}{2}$

17. $15\frac{2}{7} - 2\frac{10}{21}$

18. Find the perimeter of a rectangle with $l = 4\frac{1}{4}$ ft and $w = 3\frac{1}{2}$ ft.

Find the circumference for each circle. Use $\pi \approx \frac{22}{7}$.

19. $d = \frac{3}{8}$ mi

20. $r = 2\frac{1}{3}$ yd

21. The spinner at the right tells the number of dollars you win. Over the long run, would you expect to win, lose, or break even if each spin costs $3?

22. Thirty-five slices of chocolate cake were sold at the bake sale. If each piece was a tenth of a cake, how many cakes did they sell?

23. After school, Patsy spends $\frac{1}{2}$ of an hour on the telephone, $\frac{5}{8}$ of an hour exercising, and $\frac{3}{4}$ of an hour studying. What is the total time Patsy spends in these activities?

24. The length of a jogging trail is $5\frac{1}{2}$ miles. If you jog two-thirds of the length of the trail, how far have you jogged?

25. Amy parked in a lot that charges $3.00 for the first hour and $0.75 for each additional hour or part thereof. She parked there from 7:00 A.M. to 2:30 P.M. About how much did she pay?

1. _____

2. _____

3. _____

4. _____

5. _____

6. _____

7. _____

8. _____

9. _____

10. _____

11. _____

12. _____

13. _____

14. _____

15. _____

16. _____

17. _____

18. _____

19. _____

20. _____

21. _____

22. _____

23. _____

24. _____

25. _____

BONUS A tire has a 13-inch radius. About how far will the tire travel in 12 rotations?

Chapter 5 Test

Form 2B

Change each improper fraction to a mixed number or vice versa.

1. $\frac{108}{8}$ 2. $3\frac{4}{9}$ 3. $\frac{30}{8}$

Estimate.

4. $3\frac{7}{9} + \frac{6}{7}$ 5. $9\frac{1}{3} - 5\frac{5}{6}$ 6. $10\frac{2}{5} \div 4\frac{3}{4}$

Compute mentally.

7. $5 \times 2\frac{1}{5}$ 8. $3\frac{1}{4} \times 8$ 9. $\frac{4}{9} \times 9\frac{9}{16}$

Add, subtract, multiply, or divide. Write each answer in simplest form.

10. $\frac{3}{4} + \frac{8}{9}$ 11. $\frac{7}{8} + \frac{5}{6}$

12. $\frac{2}{3} - \frac{3}{7}$ 13. $\frac{9}{5} \times \frac{10}{27}$

14. $\frac{9}{16} \div \frac{3}{8}$ 15. $2\frac{5}{6} \div \frac{5}{6}$

16. $1\frac{1}{5} + 5\frac{1}{4}$ 17. $20\frac{5}{9} - 3\frac{5}{6}$

18. Find the perimeter of a rectangle with $l = 8\frac{1}{2}$ in. and $w = 5\frac{3}{4}$ in.

Find the circumference for each circle. Use $\pi \approx \frac{22}{7}$.

19. $d = \frac{7}{9}$ yd   20. $r = 1\frac{3}{4}$ ft

21. The spinner at the right tells the number of dollars you win. Over the long-run, would you expect to win, lose, or break even if each spin costs $3?

22. Ella walks $3\frac{1}{2}$ miles a day. How far does she walk in one week if she walks every day?

23. Rolando finds a $\frac{1}{5}$-off sale. About how much did he pay for a $39.50 golf shirt and a $51.25 pair of golf shoes?

24. The combined thickness of the pages of a textbook is $\frac{15}{16}$ inches. Each cover is $\frac{1}{8}$ of an inch thick. What is the thickness of the textbook?

25. Theresa parked in a lot that charges $4.50 for the first hour and $1.25 for each additional hour or part thereof. She parked there from 7:00 A.M. to 6:30 P.M. About how much did she pay?

BONUS A brick is put on a balance scale. The brick balances exactly with $\frac{3}{4}$ of a brick and a $\frac{3}{4}$-pound weight. How much does the brick weigh?

1. _____
2. _____
3. _____
4. _____
5. _____
6. _____
7. _____
8. _____
9. _____
10. _____
11. _____
12. _____
13. _____
14. _____
15. _____
16. _____
17. _____
18. _____
19. _____
20. _____
21. _____
22. _____
23. _____
24. _____
25. _____
_____

Use with Lessons 5-1 through 5-6 ▬▬▬▬▬

Change each improper fraction to a mixed number or vice versa.

1. $\frac{94}{8}$ **2.** $3\frac{13}{16}$

Estimate.

3. $8\frac{2}{3} + 7\frac{1}{4}$ **4.** $11\frac{7}{8} \div 3\frac{5}{6}$

Add or subtract. Write each solution in simplest form.

5. $2\frac{11}{12} + 1\frac{2}{9}$ **6.** $7\frac{3}{8} - 2\frac{2}{3}$

Add, subtract, or multiply. Write each sum, difference, or product in simplest form.

7. $\frac{5}{7} + \frac{3}{4}$

8. $\frac{5}{6} - \frac{3}{8}$

9. $\frac{8}{9} \times \frac{33}{2}$

10. Find the perimeter of a rectangle with
$l = 5\frac{2}{3}$ yd and $w = 2\frac{3}{4}$ yd.

1. _____
2. _____
3. _____
4. _____
5. _____
6. _____
7. _____
8. _____
9. _____
10. _____

Use with Lessons 5-7 through 5-11 ▬▬▬▬▬

Find the circumference for each circle. Use $\pi \approx \frac{22}{7}$.

1. $d = \frac{1}{2}$ in.   **2.** $r = 2\frac{1}{4}$ ft

3. The spinner at the right tells the
number of dollars you win. Over the
long term, would you expect to win, lose,
or break even if each spin costs 75¢?

4. In Exercise 3, over the long term,
would you expect to win, lose, or break
even if each spin costs $1?

Compute mentally.

5. $2\frac{3}{5} \times 5$ **6.** $\frac{4}{7} \times 7\frac{7}{8}$

Divide. Write each quotient in simplest form.

7. $\frac{7}{16} \div \frac{21}{32}$ **8.** $3\frac{1}{2} \div \frac{5}{8}$ **9.** $4 \div 2\frac{2}{5}$

10. Rick's test scores were 78, 98, 75, 80, 86, and 92.
Choose the best average for his test scores.
75   80   85   88   90

1. _____
2. _____
3. _____
4. _____
5. _____
6. _____
7. _____
8. _____
9. _____
10. _____

Cumulative Review Chapters 1-5

**Evaluate each expression if a = 7, b = 9, and c = 5.
(Lesson 1–8)**

1. $a + 3c$

2. $3(b - c) - 4$

Solve each equation. (Lesson 1-10)

3. $x - 27 = 57$

4. $y \div 3 = 18$

Multiply or divide. (Lessons 2-4, 2-7)

5. 0.00593×10^5

6. $0.0015 \overline{)0.0225}$

7. Divide $0.0007 \overline{)0.0348}$ Round to the nearest hundredth.
(Lesson 2-8)

8. How many meters are in 4.405 kilometers? (Lesson 2-9)

9. Make a stem-and-leaf plot for the data: 40, 18, 51, 37, 28, 32, 47, 32, and 36 at the right. (Lesson 3-6)

**Find the following for the data in Exercise 9.
(Lessons 3-3, 3-5)**

10. range

11. mode(s)

12. median

13. mean

14. Determine whether 1,992 is divisible by 2, 3, 4, 5, 6, 9, or 10. (Lesson 4-1)

15. Write the prime factorization for 96. (Lesson 4-2)

16. Identify the sequence 3, 9, 27, 81, . . . as arithmetic, geometric, or neither. Then find the next three terms of the sequence. (Lesson 4-3)

17. Find the GCF and LCM of 9 and 15. (Lesson 4-5, 4-9)

18. Express $\frac{7}{12}$ as a decimal. (Lesson 4-7).

19. What is the probability of drawing a card with a composite number on it from a deck of cards numbered 1 to 24? (Lesson 4-8)

Add, subtract, multiply, or divide. Write the answer in simplest form. (Lessons 5-3, 5-4, 5-5, 5-10)

20. $\frac{5}{6} + \frac{3}{8}$

21. $1\frac{3}{8} - \frac{5}{12}$

22. $\frac{11}{12} \times \frac{3}{22}$

23. $2\frac{3}{5} \div \frac{7}{10}$

24. Find the perimeter of a rectangle with $l = 5\frac{3}{4}$ inches and $w = 3\frac{1}{2}$ inches. (Lesson 5-6)

25. The spinner at the right tells the number of dollars you win. Over the long run, would you expect to win, lose, or break even if each spin costs $2? (Lesson 5-8)

1. _____

2. _____

3. _____

4. _____

5. _____

6. _____

7. _____

8. _____

9. _____

10. _____

11. _____

12. _____

13. _____

14. _____

15. _____

16. _____

17. _____

18. _____

19. _____

20. _____

21. _____

22. _____

23. _____

24. _____

25. _____

Glencoe Division, Macmillan/McGraw-Hill

Cumulative Test Chapters 1-5

1. Evaluate $2(b - c) + a$ if $a = 4$, $b = 9$, and $c = 6$.
   A. 34   **B.** 14   **C.** 10   **D.** 12

   1. _____

2. Divide $0.0057 \overline{)0.0951}$. Round to the nearest hundredth.
   A. 16.68   **B.** 16.69   **C.** 1.67   **D.** 1.66

   2. _____

3. Which number would appear as a stem in a stem-and-leaf plot of 49, 60, 58, 73, 67, 60, 63, 60, 64, 68, and 60?
   A. 2   **B.** 6   **C.** 1   **D.** 9

   3. _____

Find the following for the data in Exercise 3.

4. range   **A.** 24   **B.** 60   **C.** 62   **D.** 49

   4. _____

5. mode(s)   **A.** 62   **B.** 60   **C.** 24   **D.** 63

   5. _____

6. median   **A.** 62   **B.** 24   **C.** 60   **D.** 61

   6. _____

7. mean   **A.** 60   **B.** 64   **C.** 61.5   **D.** 62

   7. _____

8. Determine whether 240 is divisible by 2, 3, 4, 5, 6, 9, or 10.
   A. 2, 3, 4, 5, 6, 10   **B.** 2, 3, 4, 5, 6   **C.** 9   **D.** 10

   8. _____

9. Find the prime factorization for 195.
   A. $2 \cdot 3 \cdot 17$ **B.** $15 \cdot 13$ **C.** $3 \cdot 5 \cdot 13$ **D.** $2 \cdot 5 \cdot 13$

   9. _____

10. Find the sixth term of the sequence 8, 4, 2, 1, . . .
    A. $\frac{1}{2}$ **B.** $\frac{3}{4}$ **C.** $\frac{2}{5}$ **D.** $\frac{1}{4}$

    10. _____

11. Express $\frac{5}{8}$ as a decimal.
    A. 0.125   **B.** $0.37\overline{5}$ **C.** 0.875   **D.** 0.625

    11. _____

12. Express $\frac{57}{95}$ in simplest form.
    A. $\frac{2}{5}$ **B.** $\frac{3}{5}$ **C.** $\frac{3}{4}$ **D.** $\frac{5}{9}$

    12. _____

13. What is the probability of drawing a card with an odd number on it from a deck of cards numbered 1 through 21?
    A. $\frac{11}{21}$ **B.** $\frac{3}{7}$ **C.** $\frac{10}{21}$ **D.** $\frac{4}{7}$

    13. _____

14. Find the circumference of a circle whose radius is $\frac{3}{4}$ inch.
    A. $2\frac{5}{14}$ inches   **B.** $4\frac{3}{4}$ inches   **C.** $4\frac{5}{7}$ inches   **D.** $2\frac{1}{2}$ inches

    14. _____

Add, subtract, multiply, or divide. Write in simplest form.

15. $2\frac{3}{5} - 1\frac{2}{3}$ **A.** $1\frac{2}{5}$ **B.** $4\frac{14}{15}$ **C.** $1\frac{14}{15}$ **D.** $\frac{14}{15}$

    15. _____

16. $\frac{3}{4} + \frac{2}{5}$ **A.** $1\frac{3}{20}$ **B.** $\frac{5}{9}$ **C.** $\frac{1}{4}$ **D.** $\frac{20}{23}$

    16. _____

17. $\frac{13}{9} - \frac{1}{2}$ **A.** $\frac{12}{7}$ **B.** $\frac{5}{9}$ **C.** $\frac{17}{18}$ **D.** $\frac{35}{18}$

    17. _____

18. $3 \times 2\frac{1}{3}$ **A.** $6\frac{1}{3}$ **B.** 7   **C.** 6   **D.** $6\frac{2}{3}$

    18. _____

19. $\frac{7}{8} \times \frac{24}{35}$ **A.** $\frac{5}{3}$ **B.** $\frac{168}{280}$ **C.** $\frac{84}{140}$ **D.** $\frac{3}{5}$

    19. _____

20. $1\frac{4}{5} \div \frac{3}{10}$ **A.** 6   **B.** 7   **C.** 5   **D.** $6\frac{1}{5}$

    20. _____

Glencoe Division, Macmillan/McGraw-Hill

Form 1A

Chapter 6 Test

1. Solve $p + 2\frac{1}{2} = 10\frac{3}{4}$ by using the inverse operation.

    A. $13\frac{1}{4}$ **B.** $8\frac{1}{2}$ **C.** $8\frac{1}{4}$ **D.** $7\frac{1}{4}$

    1. _____

2. Solve $7.9 = c - 4.7$ by using the inverse operation.

    A. 2.3   **B.** 3.2   **C.** 1.26   **D.** 12.6

    2. _____

3. Solve $108 = 6e$ by using the inverse operation.

    A. 18   **B.** 102   **C.** 114   **D.** 648

    3. _____

4. What is the solution to $\frac{x}{7} = 11$?

    A. 18   **B.** 77   **C.** 4   **D.** $1\frac{4}{7}$

    4. _____

5. Solve $19 + b = 44$.

    A. 63   **B.** 24   **C.** 836   **D.** 25

    5. _____

6. Solve $81 = 3k$

    A. 27   **B.** 243   **C.** 78   **D.** 84

    6. _____

7. Solve $\frac{m}{6} = 0.9$.

    A. 6.9   **B.** 5.1   **C.** 5.4   **D.** $6\frac{2}{3}$

    7. _____

8. Solve $f + 12.8 = 14.1$.

    A. 1.3   **B.** 26.9   **C.** 2.69   **D.** 180.48

    8. _____

9. Solve $y - 6 = 102$.

    A. 612   **B.** 108   **C.** 17   **D.** 96

    9. _____

10. Solve $r \div \frac{1}{4} = \frac{1}{2}$.

    A. $\frac{1}{8}$ **B.** $\frac{1}{4}$ **C.** $\frac{1}{2}$ **D.** 2

    10. _____

11. Solve $\frac{l}{0.8} = 1.6$.

    A. 2   **B.** 0.8   **C.** 1.28   **D.** 2.4

    11. _____

12. Translate *fifteen less than w* into an algebraic expression.

    A. $w + 15$ **B.** $w - 15$ **C.** $15 - w$ **D.** $15 + w$

    12. _____

13. Translate *h increased by 9* into an algebraic expression.

    A. $h - 9$ **B.** $9h$ **C.** $h \div 9$ **D.** $h + 9$

    13. _____

14. Translate *the difference of 2 and d* into an algebraic expression.

    A. $2 - d$ **B.** $2 + d$ **C.** $2d$ **D.** $d - 2$

    14. _____

Form 1A (continued) ▬▬▬▬▬▬

15. Translate *the product of 7 and m* into an algebraic expression.   15. _____

    A. $7 + m$ **B.** $7m$ **C.** $7 \div m$ **D.** $7 - m$

16. Complete 3.5 tons = ■ lb.   16. _____

    A. 7,000   **B.** 3,000   **C.** 3,500   **D.** 6,500

17. Complete ■ c = 2.5 pt.   17. _____

    A. 10   **B.** 7.5   **C.** 5   **D.** 1.25

18. How many quarts are in $4\frac{1}{2}$ gallons?   18. _____

    A. 16   **B.** 2.25   **C.** 9   **D.** 18

19. Change 1.5 pounds to ounces.   19. _____

    A. 3   **B.** 24   **C.** 12   **D.** 36

Find the area of each figure in Exercises 20 and 21.

20. [rectangle: 0.8 m by 3.2 m]   **A.** 2.56 m^2 **B.** 3.0 m^2 20. _____
                                          C. 8.0 m^2 **D.** 4.0 m^2

21. [parallelogram: 0.8 cm height, 1.4 cm side, 2.4 cm base]   **A.** 2.0 cm^2 **B.** 3.36 cm^2 21. _____
                                          C. 7.6 cm^2 **D.** 1.92 cm^2

22. Find the area of the parallelogram with a base of 3.5 meters   22. _____
and a height of 6 meters.

    A. 21.0 m^2 **B.** 19 m^2 **C.** 9.5 m^2 **D.** 3.5 m^2

23. What is the length of a rectangle with an area of 23.8 square   23. _____
miles and a width of 3.5 miles?

    A. 8.4 mi   **B.** 7.5 mi   **C.** 6.8 mi   **D.** 4.8 mi

24. Edwin's mother is 57 years old. Her age is three years more   24. _____
than twice Edwin's age. What is Edwin's age?

    A. 30 years   **B.** 27 years   **C.** 15 years   **D.** 37 years

25. A number is divided by 6. Then the quotient is decreased by 1.   25. _____
If the result is 3, what was the original number?

    A. 19   **B.** 11   **C.** 12   **D.** 24

BONUS Solve $\frac{2}{3}x = 3\frac{1}{4}$.   _____

    A. 0.33   **B.** 2.1   **C.** 4.875   **D.** 2.625

Form 1B _____   *Chapter 6 Test*

1. Solve $2\frac{1}{4} + k = 11\frac{1}{2}$ by using the inverse operation.

   A. $9\frac{1}{4}$ **B.** $13\frac{3}{4}$ **C.** $9\frac{1}{2}$ **D.** $5\frac{1}{10}$

   1. _____

2. Solve $r - 8.9 = 9.8$ by using the inverse operation.

   A. 0.9   **B.** 1.1   **C.** 18.7   **D.** 87.22

   2. _____

3. Solve $15 = \frac{m}{5}$ by using the inverse operation.

   A. 3   **B.** 10   **C.** 20   **D.** 75

   3. _____

4. What is the solution to $8v = 136$?

   A. 128   **B.** 17   **C.** 144   **D.** 1088

   4. _____

5. Solve $23 + d = 51$.

   A. 28   **B.** 74   **C.** 47   **D.** 82

   5. _____

6. Solve $0.8 = \frac{u}{4}$.

   A. 0.2   **B.** 4.8   **C.** 3.2   **D.** 0.2

   6. _____

7. Solve $3j = 2.7$.

   A. 8.1   **B.** 0.3   **C.** 0.9   **D.** 5.7

   7. _____

8. Solve $24.2 = w + 6.2$.

   A. 18.0   **B.** 30.4   **C.** 3.9   **D.** 20.0

   8. _____

9. Solve $144 = e - 9$.

   A. 135   **B.** 153   **C.** 16   **D.** 1,296

   9. _____

10. Solve $z \div \frac{1}{3} = \frac{6}{7}$.

    A. $\frac{6}{21}$ **B.** $\frac{18}{7}$ **C.** $\frac{11}{21}$ **D.** $\frac{2}{7}$

    10. _____

11. Solve $\frac{b}{0.7} = 2.8$.

    A. 1.96   **B.** 4.0   **C.** 2.1   **D.** 3.5

    11. _____

12. Translate *the quotient of x and 5* into an algebraic expression.

    A. $x - 5$ **B.** $x + 5$ **C.** $\frac{x}{5}$ **D.** $5 \div x$

    12. _____

13. Translate *sixteen minus i* into an algebraic expression.

    A. $i - 16$ **B.** $16 - i$ **C.** $16 + i$ **D.** $i \div 16$

    13. _____

14. Translate *the sum of q and 11* into an algebraic expression.

    A. $11q$ **B.** $q \div 11$ **C.** $q - 11$ **D.** $q + 11$

    14. _____

Glencoe Division, Macmillan/McGraw-Hill

15. Translate *twelve times a number* into an algebraic expression. 15. _____

    A. $12 + x$ **B.** $12 - x$ **C.** $12 \div x$ **D.** $12x$

16. Complete 9,000 lb = ■ tons. 16. _____

    A. 3   **B.** 4.5   **C.** 3.5   **D.** 4

17. Complete ■ pt = 3 qt. 17. _____

    A. 6   **B.** 12   **C.** 18   **D.** 7.5

18. How many cups are in $4\frac{1}{2}$ pints? 18. _____

    A. 2.25   **B.** 8   **C.** 9   **D.** 10

19. Change $5\frac{1}{2}$ pounds to ounces. 19. _____

    A. 66   **B.** 22   **C.** 88   **D.** 90

Find the area of each figure in Exercises 20 and 21.

20.   0.7 m   1.2 m   3.8 m   **A.** 2.66 m²   **B.** 4.56 m² 20. _____
                                            C. 10 m²   **D.** 9.0 m²

21. 0.8 cm   3.4 cm   **A.** 8.4 cm²   **B.** 4.2 cm² 21. _____
                                         C. 3.0 cm²   **D.** 2.72 cm²

22. Find the area of the rectangle with a length of 12.5 feet 22. _____
and a width of 8.0 feet.

    A. 100 ft²   **B.** 41 ft²   **C.** 50 ft²   **D.** 20.5 ft²

23. What is the base of a parallelogram with an area of 30.5 square 23. _____
miles and a height of 5 miles?

    A. 152.5 mi   **B.** 25.5 mi   **C.** 35.5 mi   **D.** 6.1 mi

24. The Ruizs sold a valuable sculpture for $28,000. This price is 24. _____
$10,000 more than three times the amount they originally
paid for it. How much did they originally pay for it?

    A. $60,000   **B.** $6,000   **C.** $12,600   **D.** $13,000

25. Paddy's father is 45 years old. His age is five years more than 25. _____
four times Paddy's age. What is Paddy's age?

    A. 13 years   **B.** 12 years   **C.** 10 years   **D.** 11 years

BONUS Write an algebraic expression for the product of two _____
consecutive odd whole numbers. Let $x + 1$ be the lesser number.

    A. $x(x + 1)$ **B.** $(x + 1)(x + 4)$
    C. $x(x + 3)$ **D.** $(x + 1)(x + 3)$

Form 2A

Solve each equation by using the inverse operation.

1. $x + 4.9 = 12.2$ 2. $\frac{e}{1.9} = 2.7$

3. What is the solution to $3.6t = 11.52$?

Solve each equation. Check your solution.

4. $16 + a = 43$ 5. $c - 25 = 9$

6. $12\frac{1}{2} = r - 6\frac{1}{3}$ 7. $s + 3.7 = 15.2$

8. $51 = 3m$ 9. $\frac{n}{4} = 15$

10. $1.4j = 0.7$ 11. $\frac{1}{2}w = \frac{3}{8}$

Translate each phrase into an algebraic expression.

12. twelve more than z 13. l decreased by 10

14. thirteen times y 15. the quotient of d and 5

Complete.

16. 6 pt = _?_ qt   17. _?_ ton = 1,000 lb

18. Change 5 lb to ounces.   19. Change 12 cups to pints.

Find the area of each figure.

20.

1.2 mm

2.3 mm

21.

3 yd

5 yd

7 yd

22. rectangle: $l = 6.5$ cm; $w = 3.4$ cm

23. parallelogram: base = 10.5 feet; height = 8 feet.

Solve by using an equation.

24. A number is multiplied by 4. Then this product is increased by 7. If the answer is 91, what was the original number?

25. The Leungs sold a valuable painting for $55,000. This price is $1,000 more than twice the amount they originally paid for it. How much did they originally pay for it?

BONUS If j represents Jami's age and r represents Rita's age in years, write a sentence in words that explains the meaning of $j = r - 4$.

1. _____

2. _____

3. _____

4. _____

5. _____

6. _____

7. _____

8. _____

9. _____

10. _____

11. _____

12. _____

13. _____

14. _____

15. _____

16. _____

17. _____

18. _____

19. _____

20. _____

21. _____

22. _____

23. _____

24. _____

25. _____

_____

Chapter 6 Test

Form 2B _____

Solve each equation by using the inverse operation.

1. $r - 3.9 = 9.3$ **2.** $4.1m = 13.12$

3. What is the solution to $6\frac{1}{4} = s - \frac{7}{2}$?

Solve each equation. Check your solution.

4. $37 + e = 44$ **5.** $11 = p - 20$

6. $k + 4.8 = 11.3$ **7.** $x - 5\frac{1}{2} = 13\frac{1}{4}$

8. $\frac{c}{5} = 16$ **9.** $84 = 7d$

10. $12z = 0.6$ **11.** $\frac{1}{5} = \frac{1}{2}u$

Translate each phrase into an algebraic expression.

12. twenty less j **13.** the sum of x and 3

14. 9 divided into f **15.** the product of 2 and t

Complete.

16. 0.5 qt = _?_ pt   **17.** 16 fl oz = _?_ c

18. How many quarts are in $2\frac{1}{2}$ gallons?

19. Change 1.5 tons to pounds.

Find the area of each figure.

20.

0.8 cm
3.3 cm

21.

4.5 ft   6.2 ft
9.0 ft

22. parallelogram: $b = 11.6$ ft; $h = 10.3$ ft

23. What is the length of a rectangle with an area of 40 square feet and a width of 5 feet?

Solve by using an equation.

24. In the 1990–91 season, Reggie Lewis scored the most points for the Boston Celtics with 1,478 points and an 18.7 points per game average for 79 games. The runner-up, Larry Bird, had a 19.4 points per game average for 60 games. Bird scored 314 points less than Lewis. How many points did Bird score?

25. The number of infielders on a baseball team is one less than three times the number of pitchers. If there are eleven infielders, how many pitchers are there?

BONUS One-third of Connie's age decreased by 1 is Rick's age. Rick is 15 years old. What is Connie's age?

1. _____
2. _____
3. _____
4. _____
5. _____
6. _____
7. _____
8. _____
9. _____
10. _____
11. _____
12. _____
13. _____
14. _____
15. _____
16. _____
17. _____
18. _____
19. _____
20. _____
21. _____
22. _____
23. _____
24. _____
25. _____
_____

Use with Lessons 6-1 through 6-4 ━━━━━━━━━━

Solve each equation by using the inverse operation.

1. $72 = \frac{c}{6}$

2. $2\frac{3}{4} = x + \frac{1}{2}$

Solve each equation. Check your solution.

3. $p + 58 = 73$

4. $105 = y - 17$

5. $16\frac{3}{8} + e = 41$

6. $9m = 81$

7. $\frac{n}{3} = 2.6$

8. $1.3z = 3.9$

Translate each phrase into an algebraic expression.

9. Mike's score increased by 9

10. twelve fewer points than the New York Giants

1. _____
2. _____
3. _____
4. _____
5. _____
6. _____
7. _____
8. _____
9. _____
10. _____

- -

Use with Lessons 6-5 through 6-7 ━━━━━━━━━━

Complete each sentence.

1. $7 \text{ c} = \underline{\ ?\ } \text{ pt}$

2. $\underline{\ ?\ } \text{ gal} = 14 \text{ qt}$

3. $1\frac{1}{2} \text{ lb} = \underline{\ ?\ } \text{ oz}$

4. $\underline{\ ?\ } \text{ mi} = 13,200 \text{ ft}$

5. How many quarts are in 11 pints?

Find the area of each figure.

6.

2.3 mm

1.7 mm

7.

1.7 cm

2.4 cm

3.9 cm

8. What is the length of a rectangle with an area of 36 square yards and a width of 4.5 yards?

9. A number is multiplied by 8. Then 13 is added to the result. If the result is 57, what was the original number?

10. The number of forwards on a basketball team is two less than twice the number of guards. If there are 4 forwards on the team, how many guards are there?

1. _____
2. _____
3. _____
4. _____
5. _____
6. _____
7. _____
8. _____
9. _____
10. _____

Glencoe Division, Macmillan/McGraw-Hill

Cumulative Review Chapters 1-6

1. Evaluate $3a - b$ if $a = 7$ and $b = 9$. (Lesson 1-8)
2. Divide $0.005 \overline{)0.000291}$. Round to the nearest hundredth. (Lesson 2-8)
3. Make a line plot for the data
   33, 36, 37, 36, 34, 35, 36,
   at the right. (Lesson 3-4)

Find the following for the data in Exercise 3.
(Lessons 3-3, 3-5)

4. range
5. mode(s)
6. median
7. mean
8. Identify the sequence 1, 4, 9, 16, 25, . . . as arithmetic, geometric, or neither. Then find the next three terms of the sequence. (Lesson 4-3)
9. Find the GCF and LCM of 24 and 40. (Lessons 4-5, 4-9)
10. Express $\frac{2}{3}$ as a decimal. (Lesson 4-7)
11. Express 0.875 as a fraction in simplest form. (Lesson 4-7)

A bag of marbles contains 7 red, 16 clear, 12 black, 10 blue, and 15 yellow marbles. If you reach in the bag and draw one marble at random, what is the probability that you will draw

12. a yellow marble? (Lesson 4-8)
13. either a black or yellow marble? (Lesson 4-8)
14. The length of a jogging trail is $5\frac{1}{2}$ miles. If you jog three-fifths of the length of the trail, how many miles do you have left to complete the trail? (Lesson 5-11)
15. Find the perimeter of a rectangle with $l = 5\frac{3}{4}$ feet and $w = 3\frac{1}{2}$ feet. (Lesson 5-6)
16. Find the circumference of a circle whose diameter is 2.75 millimeters. (Lesson 5-7)
17. Translate *ten less than y* into an algebraic expression. (Lesson 6-4)
18. How many pints are in $5\frac{1}{2}$ quarts? (Lesson 6-6)
19. Find the area of a parallelogram with $b = 7$ feet; $h = 3.5$ feet. (Lesson 6-7)

Solve each equation. Write each solution in simplest form.
(Lessons 5-3, 5-10, 6-1, 6-3)

20. $\frac{3}{5} + \frac{5}{9} = a$
21. $b = 2\frac{7}{12} \div \frac{3}{8}$
22. $1\frac{5}{8} = c + \frac{3}{4}$
23. $\frac{d}{3.5} = 0.6$
24. $1.3e = 3.9$
25. $\frac{7}{8} = \frac{1}{2}f$

1. _____
2. _____
3. _____
4. _____
5. _____
6. _____
7. _____
8. _____
9. _____
10. _____
11. _____
12. _____
13. _____
14. _____
15. _____
16. _____
17. _____
18. _____
19. _____
20. _____
21. _____
22. _____
23. _____
24. _____
25. _____

Cumulative Test Chapters 1-6

1. Evaluate $2(a - b) - 6$ if $a = 8$ and $b = 5$.
   A. 12   B. 20   C. 0   D. 32

2. $10^6 \times 0.000759$ A. 7,590   B. 759,000   C. 75.9   D. 759

**Use the stem-and-leaf plot to find each measure in
Exercises 3 through 6.**

3. range   A. 38   B. 36   C. 2   D. 22
4. mode(s)   A. 22   B. 26   C. 20.4   D. 38
5. median   A. 20.4   B. 26   C. 24   D. 22
6. mean   A. 19   B. 26   C. 20.4   D. 22

0	25
1	89
2	2226
3	08

7. Find the next term in the sequence 60, 61, 63, 66, 70, ...
   A. 75   B. 73   C. 76   D. 80

8. Express $\frac{5}{6}$ as a decimal.
   A. 0.83   B. $0.\overline{8}$ C. $0.8\overline{3}$ D. 0.8

9. Express 0.375 as a fraction in simplest form.
   A. $\frac{1}{6}$ B. $\frac{1}{3}$ C. $\frac{3}{5}$ D. $\frac{3}{8}$

10. Find the perimeter of a rectangle with $l = 8\frac{3}{4}$ yards and
    $w = 6\frac{2}{3}$ yards.

    A. $15\frac{5}{12}$ yd   B. $30\frac{5}{6}$ yd   C. $58\frac{1}{3}$ yd   D. 30 yd

11. Find the circumference of a circle whose radius is 2.5 miles.
    A. 15.7 mi   B. 5 mi   C. 15 mi   D. 7.85 mi

12. Translate *e increased by 12* into an algebraic expression.
    A. $e - 12$ B. $12e$ C. $e + 12$ D. $12 - e$

13. Molly's father is 35 years old. His age is four years less than
    three times Molly's age. What is Molly's age?
    A. 17 years   B. 10 years   C. 16 years   D. 13 years

14. Find the area of the parallelogram with a base of
    6.75 meters and a height of 8.00 meters.
    A. 7.375 m^2 B. 54 m^2 C. 29.5 m^2 D. 14.75 m^2

Solve each equation. Write each solution in simplest form.

15. $10\frac{1}{4} = a - 6\frac{1}{3}$ A. 3.95   B. $3\frac{11}{12}$ C. $16\frac{7}{12}$ D. $16\frac{11}{12}$

16. $b + 4.7 = 16.3$ A. 3.5   B. 21.0   C. 35.0   D. 11.6

17. $0.9 = \frac{c}{3.3}$ A. 2.97   B. 2.7   C. 4.2   D. 0.297

18. $\frac{d}{6} = \frac{5}{8}$ A. $\frac{5}{48}$ B. $\frac{4}{15}$ C. $3\frac{3}{4}$ D. 22

19. $57 = 1.9e$ A. 3   B. 30   C. 55.1   D. 5.51

20. $f = 3\frac{1}{7} \div \frac{11}{14}$ A. 4   B. 17   C. $2\frac{23}{49}$ D. 3

1. _____
2. _____
3. _____
4. _____
5. _____
6. _____
7. _____
8. _____
9. _____
10. _____
11. _____
12. _____
13. _____
14. _____
15. _____
16. _____
17. _____
18. _____
19. _____
20. _____

Form 1A

1. Name the integer represented by *G*. Then find its opposite and its absolute value.

1. _____

$$\begin{array}{c} G \\ \leftarrow\!\!+\!\!\bullet\!\!+\!\!+\!\!+\!\!+\!\!+\!\!\rightarrow \\ \begin{array}{ccccccc} -3 & -2 & -1 & 0 & 1 & 2 \end{array} \end{array}$$

A. 3; -3; 3　　**B.** -3; 3; 3　**C.** -3; -3; 3　　**D.** -3; -3; -3

2. 10 ● -10

2. _____

A. >　　　　**B.** <　　　**C.** =　　　**D.** +

3. -11 ● 0

3. _____

A. >　　　　**B.** <　　　**C.** =　　　**D.** +

4. Order 3, -4, 0, 1, and -2 from least to greatest.

4. _____

A. 3, 1, 0, -2, -4　　　　**B.** 3, 1, 0, -4, -2
C. -4, -2, 0, 1, 3　　　　**D.** -2, -4, 0, 1, 3

Use the graph to name the ordered pair for each point.

5. *Q*

5. _____

A. (0, 3)　　**B.** (2, -3)
C. (-2, -3)　**D.** (-2, 3)

6. *E*

6. _____

A. (0, 3)　　**B.** (2, -3)
C. (3, 0)　　**D.** (-3, 0)

7. *P*

7. _____

A. (-2, -3)　**B.** (-3, -2)
C. (3, -2)　　**D.** (-3, 2)

8. *B*

8. _____

A. (-1, -4)　**B.** (-1, 4)
C. (-4, 1)　　**D.** (1, -4)

Solve each equation.

9. $w = 11 + (-7)$

9. _____

A. 4　　　**B.** -4　　　**C.** -18　　　**D.** 18

10. $x = -5(-11)$

10. _____

A. 16　　**B.** -16　　**C.** 55　　　**D.** -55

11. $m = 13 - 19$

11. _____

A. -247　**B.** 247　　**C.** 6　　　**D.** -6

12. $-1 + 1 = n$

12. _____

A. 2　　　**B.** 0　　　**C.** -2　　　**D.** -1

13. $y = (-56) \div 7$

13. _____

A. 8　　　**B.** -49　　**C.** 49　　　**D.** -8

Glencoe Division, Macmillan/McGraw-Hill

Chapter 7 Test Form 1A (continued)

14. $p = (-9)^2$

    A. 18   **B.** 81   **C.** -81   **D.** -18

14. _____

15. $0 = u + 5$

    A. 10   **B.** 0   **C.** 5   **D.** -5

15. _____

16. $7 = \frac{v}{-3}$

    A. $-2\frac{1}{3}$ **B.** -21   **C.** 4   **D.** 21

16. _____

17. $-37 - 8 = c$

    A. 45   **B.** -35   **C.** -45   **D.** 296

17. _____

18. $\frac{e}{5} = -6$

    A. 30   **B.** -30   **C.** -1   **D.** $-1\frac{1}{5}$

18. _____

19. $-48 = -24b$

    A. 2   **B.** -2   **C.** -24   **D.** 0.5

19. _____

20. Write 3×10^{-2} in standard form.

    A. 0.3   **B.** 0.03   **C.** 3   **D.** 0.003

20. _____

21. Write 0.0009 in scientific notation.

    A. 9×10^{-3} **B.** 9×10^{-5} **C.** 9×10^{-4} **D.** 9×10^{-2}

21. _____

22. Choose the equation and solution for the following:
When a number r is multiplied by -5, the result is -35.

    A. $-5r = -35; r = 7$ **B.** $5r = -35; r = -7$
    C. $r + (-5) = -35; r = -30$ **D.** $r + 5 = -35; r = -40$

22. _____

23. Choose the equation and solution for the following:
If you decrease a number by 4, the result is -11.

    A. $n + 4 = -11; n = -7$ **B.** $4 - n = -11; n = 15$
    C. $4 + n = -11; n = -15$ **D.** $n - 4 = -11; n = -7$

23. _____

24. Find the decimals for $1 \div 9$, $1 \div 99$, and $1 \div 999$. Use this pattern to predict $1 \div 9,999$.

    A. $0.\overline{0001}$
    C. $0.\overline{000001}$
    B. $0.\overline{00001}$
    D. $0.\overline{0000001}$

24. _____

25. Carlos jogged 2 miles on the first day. Then each day after that he jogged 3.5, 5.5, 7, and 9 miles. How many days should it take to exceed 13 miles in one day?

    A. 7   **B.** 6   **C.** 5   **D.** 8

25. _____

BONUS Give the next number in the pattern: 2, 9, 23, 44, _?_, . . .

    A. 72   **B.** 79   **C.** 308   **D.** 65

_____

Glencoe Division, Macmillan/McGraw-Hill

1. Name the integer represented by *H*. Then find its opposite and its absolute value.

   H
   ←—●—|—|—|—|—→
   -2 -1   0   1

   A. -1; -1; 1   **B.** 1; -1; 1   **C.** -1; 1; 1   **D.** -1; 1; -1

   1._____

2. -30 ● -20

   A. >   **B.** <   **C.** =   **D.** +

   2._____

3. 0 ● -15

   A. >   **B.** <   **C.** =   **D.** +

   3._____

4. Order -3, 5, 0, -1, and 1 from greatest to least.

   A. -3, -1, 0, 1, 5   **B.** 5, 1, 0, -3, -1
   C. -1, -3, 0, 1, 5   **D.** 5, 1, 0, -1, -3

   4._____

Use the graph to name the ordered pair for each point.

5. *J*

   A. (0, -2)   **B.** (0, 2)
   C. (-2, 0)   **D.** (2, 0)

   5._____

6. *M*

   A. (-3, 3)   **B.** (3, 3)
   C. (-3, -3)   **D.** (3, -3)

   6._____

7. *R*

   A. (2, 4)   **B.** (4, 2)
   C. (2, 3)   **D.** (2, -4)

   7._____

8. *T*

   A. (1, -4)   **B.** (-1, -4)
   C. (-1, 4)   **D.** (-4, -1)

   8._____

Solve each equation.

9. $e = -6 + 10$

   A. 4   **B.** -4   **C.** -60   **D.** 16

   9._____

10. $y = -12(-8)$

    A. -20   **B.** 20   **C.** 1.5   **D.** 96

    10._____

11. $10 - 18 = i$

    A. 8   **B.** -8   **C.** 28   **D.** -28

    11._____

12. $f = -3 + 3$

    A. 6   **B.** -6   **C.** 0   **D.** -9

    12._____

13. $(-36) \div 6 = n$

    A. -6   **B.** 6   **C.** 30   **D.** -216

    13._____

14. $(-7)^2 = a$

    A. 49   **B.** -14   **C.** -49   **D.** -9

    14._____

Glencoe Division, Macmillan/McGraw-Hill

Chapter 7 Test Form 1B (continued)

15. $w + 4 = 0$

    A. 0   **B.** 4   **C.** -4   **D.** 5

15. _____

16. $\frac{c}{-7} = 5$

    A. 35   **B.** -2   **C.** 2   **D.** -35

16. _____

17. $p = -9 - 18$

    A. -27   **B.** 27   **C.** -9   **D.** 0.5

17. _____

18. $\frac{s}{8} = -8$

    A. 64   **B.** -64   **C.** 0   **D.** -1

18. _____

19. $-91 = -13z$

    A. -7   **B.** -78   **C.** 7   **D.** $0.\overline{142857}$

19. _____

20. Write 8×10^{-1} in standard form.

    A. 0.08   **B.** 8.0   **C.** 0.8   **D.** 0.008

20. _____

21. Write 0.00007 in scientific notation.

    A. 7×10^{-5} **B.** 7×10^{-4} **C.** 7×10^{-3} **D.** 7×10^{-2}

21. _____

22. Choose the equation and solution for the following:
When a number is divided by 3, the result is -18.

    A. $n \div 3 = 18; n = -6$ **B.** $3n = 18; n = 3$
    C. $n \div 3 = -18; n = -54$ **D.** $n \div 3 = -18; n = 6$

22. _____

23. Choose the equation and solution for the following:
If you increase a number by 12, the result is -25.

    A. $x - 12 = -25; x = -13$ **B.** $x + 12 = -25; x = -13$
    C. $x - 12 = -25; x = -37$ **D.** $x + 12 = -25; x = -37$

23. _____

24. Look at the pattern shown in the box. Use this pattern to find the two numbers whose sum is 10,000,002.

| $48 + 54 = 102$ |
| $448 + 554 = 1{,}002$ |
| $4{,}448 + 5{,}554 = 10{,}002$ |

    A. 55,554; 44,448   **B.** 5,555,554; 4,444,448
    C. 555,554; 444,448   **D.** 55,555,554; 44,444,448

24. _____

25. Suppose February 1 is a Saturday and it is a leap year. What is the date of the next to last Saturday in February?

    A. 29   **B.** 21   **C.** 22   **D.** 23

25. _____

BONUS Complete the pattern: 12, 21, 34, 43, _?_, _?_, . . .

    A. 65, 56   **B.** 45, 56   **C.** 56, 65   **D.** 67, 76

_____

Chapter 7 Test

Form 2A

Write the integer represented by each letter. Then find its opposite and its absolute value.

1. A
2. B
3. C

-6 -5 -4 -3 -2 -1 0 1 2 3 4 5 6

Replace each ● with $<$, $>$, or $=$.

4. -8 ● 8

5. -4 ● -40

6. -9 ● 0

7. On the same day, the thermometer registered 10°F below zero in Duluth and 7°F below zero in St. Paul. Which city is warmer?

On the coordinate plane, graph and label each point.

8. $Q(2, 3)$

9. $R(3, -2)$

10. $P(0, -4)$

11. $S(-4, -1)$

Solve each equation.

12. $c = 6 + (-2)$

13. $r = 11(-3)$

14. $j = 12 - 19$

15. $s = -9 + 9$

16. $-7(-8) = i$

17. $(-3)^2 = t$

18. $n = (-37) + (-8)$

19. $(-42) \div 7 = d$

20. $z = -72 \div (-4)$

21. $r + 9 = 0$

22. $\frac{m}{-3} = 5$

23. $\frac{w}{8} = -3$

24. $-12a = -36$

25. $-3 = k - 8$

26. At Franklin School, the bell rings at 8:03, 8:49, 8:55, 9:41, 9:47, and 10:33. When will the bell ring next?

27. Write 6×10^{-4} in standard form.

28. Write 0.000005 in scientific notation.

29. Write an equation for the following. Then solve. The product of 0.2 and a number x is -1.6.

30. Find the decimals for $\frac{1}{11}$, $\frac{1}{111}$, and $\frac{1}{1111}$. Use this pattern to predict $\frac{1}{11,111}$.

BONUS Complete the pattern: 3, 6, 11, 18, 27, 38, __?__, __?__, . . .

1. _____
2. _____
3. _____
4. _____
5. _____
6. _____
7. _____
8. _____
9. _____
10. _____
11. _____
12. _____
13. _____
14. _____
15. _____
16. _____
17. _____
18. _____
19. _____
20. _____
21. _____
22. _____
23. _____
24. _____
25. _____
26. _____
27. _____
28. _____
29. _____
30. _____

Form 2B _____

Write the integer represented by each letter. Then find its opposite and its absolute value.

1. Q
2. R
3. P

Replace each ● with <, >, or =.

4. -7 ● -5   5. 10 ● -10   6. 0 ● -35

7. On the same day, the thermometer registered 0°F in Casper and 3°F below zero in Boise. Which city is colder?

On the coordinate plane, graph and label each point.

8. $W(0, 3)$
9. $Y(-1, 4)$
10. $Z(-2, -3)$
11. $X(3, -2)$

Solve each equation.

12. $r = 9 + (-5)$
13. $s = -6(-12)$
14. $k = 11 - 18$
15. $-7 + 7 = f$
16. $-9(7) = j$
17. $(-5)^2 = p$
18. $m = (-8) + (-24)$
19. $d = (-72) \div 8$
20. $x = -48 \div (-3)$
21. $0 = y + 2$
22. $6 = \frac{i}{-2}$
23. $\frac{w}{9} = -4$
24. $-81 = -27c$
25. $-8 = l - 13$

26. Andrea did 6 sit-ups on the first day. Then each day after that she did 7, 9, 12, 16, and 21 sit-ups. How many sit-ups should she do on the seventh day if she wants to follow this same pattern?

27. Write 5×10^{-3} in standard form.

28. Write 0.0000003 in scientific notation.

29. Write an equation for the following. Then solve. The sum of a number e and -6 is 13.

30. Suppose May 1 is a Friday, what is the date of the last Friday in May?

BONUS Find the sum of the first 50 positive odd numbers.

1. _____
2. _____
3. _____
4. _____
5. _____
6. _____
7. _____
8. _____
9. _____
10. _____
11. _____
12. _____
13. _____
14. _____
15. _____
16. _____
17. _____
18. _____
19. _____
20. _____
21. _____
22. _____
23. _____
24. _____
25. _____
26. _____
27. _____
28. _____
29. _____
30. _____
_____

Use with Lessons 7-1 through 7-5

Find the opposite and absolute value of each integer.

1. -19 2. 25

3. Order the integers 3, 0, –2, 4, –4, and –1 from least to greatest.

On the coordinate plane, graph and label each point.

4. $S(4, 0)$ 5. $R(-2, -3)$

6. $T(3, -2)$

Solve each equation.

7. $a = -25 + (-12)$

8. $6 + (-9) = b$

9. $c = -11 - 46$

10. $d = 7 - (-25)$

1. _____
2. _____
3. _____
4. _____
5. _____
6. _____
7. _____
8. _____
9. _____
10. _____

Use with Lessons 7-6 through 7-10

Solve each equation.

1. $e = -7(-14)$ 2. $-8(12) = f$

3. $-44 \div (-11) = g$ 4. $h = -140 \div 7$

5. $-56 = \frac{i}{2}$ 6. $25 + j = -75$

7. The quotient when a number k is divided by –4 is –11. Write an equation for the problem and solve.

8. Write 2×10^{-7} in standard form.

9. Write 0.000000002 in scientific notation.

10. At the Truman School, the bell rings at 8:06, 8:52, 8:56, 9:42, 9:46, and 10:32. When will the bell ring next?

1. _____
2. _____
3. _____
4. _____
5. _____
6. _____
7. _____
8. _____
9. _____
10. _____

Cumulative Review Chapters 1-7

1. Evaluate $(21 + 78) \div 9 + 2 \cdot 7$. (Lesson 1-7)
2. Order 1.10, 1.01, 11.1, 10.1, and 1 from least to greatest. (Lesson 2-1)
3. Write 2,070,000,000 in scientific notation. (Lesson 2-6)

In Exercises 4 through 6, find the following for the data 11, 11, 7, 5, 7, 9, and 13. (Lesson 3-5)

4. mode(s) 5. median 6. mean
7. Identify the sequence 79, 73, 67, 61, . . . as arithmetic, geometric, or neither. Then find the next three terms of the sequence. (Lesson 4-3)
8. Express $\frac{5}{6}$ as a decimal. (Lesson 4-7)
9. Express 0.125 as a fraction in simplest form. (Lesson 4-7)

A bag of marbles contains 3 red, 12 clear, 8 black, 6 blue, and 11 yellow marbles. If you reach into the bag and draw one marble at random, what is the probability that you will draw

10. a clear marble? (Lesson 4-8)
11. either a black or blue marble? (Lesson 4-8)
12. Find the perimeter of a rectangle with $l = 6\frac{1}{3}$ yards and $w = 4\frac{2}{3}$ yards. (Lesson 5-6)
13. Cossette wants to fill an 8-gallon container with spring water. If she uses a $1\frac{1}{2}$-gallon container, how many times must it be refilled? (Lesson 5-10)
14. Find the circumference of a circle whose radius is $\frac{1}{4}$ inch. (Lesson 5-7)
15. Translate *the quotient of c and 11* into an algebraic expression. (Lesson 6-4)
16. How many quarts are in $3\frac{1}{2}$ gallons? (Lesson 6-6)
17. Find the area of a parallelogram with $b = 12.2$ cm; $h = 8.5$ cm. (Lesson 6-7)
18. At the Foss School, the bell rings at 8:06, 8:52, 8:58, 9:44, 9:50, and 10:36. When will the next bell ring? (Lesson 7-6)
19. Write an equation for the following. The product of 0.3 and a number t is -0.63. Then solve. (Lesson 7-9)

Solve each equation. Check your solution. (Lessons 5-3, 5-10, 6-1, 6-3, 7-9)

20. $\frac{5}{8} + \frac{5}{6} = a$
21. $b = 1\frac{1}{2} \div 2\frac{1}{4}$
22. $c - \frac{7}{8} = 2\frac{1}{16}$
23. $6.8 = 1.7d$
24. $48 = \frac{e}{-3}$
25. $-7 = f - 3$

1. _____
2. _____
3. _____
4. _____
5. _____
6. _____
7. _____
8. _____
9. _____
10. _____
11. _____
12. _____
13. _____
14. _____
15. _____
16. _____
17. _____
18. _____
19. _____
20. _____
21. _____
22. _____
23. _____
24. _____
25. _____

Glencoe Division, Macmillan/McGraw-Hill

Cumulative Test Chapters 1-7

1. Evaluate $(87 - 37) \div 2 + 8 \cdot 6$.   1. _____
   A. 73   **B.** 30   **C.** $\frac{5}{6}$ **D.** 148

2. Divide $0.002 \overline{)0.000751}$. Round to the nearest hundredth.   2. _____
   A. 3.8   **B.** 0.38   **C.** 38   **D.** 0.038

3. How many milligrams are in 0.036 kilograms?   3. _____
   A. 3,600   **B.** 3.6   **C.** 36,000   **D.** 36

In Exercises 4 through 6, find the following for the data 5.6, 6.7, 8.4, 9.3, 7.8, 8.8, 9.0, 8.2, and 8.6.

4. mode(s)   **A.** 7.8   **B.** 8.2   **C.** 8.6   **D.** none   4. _____

5. median   **A.** 8.03   **B.** 8.2   **C.** 8.05   **D.** 8.4   5. _____

6. mean   **A.** 8.04   **B.** 8.2   **C.** 8.05   **D.** 3   6. _____

7. Find the sixth term in the sequence 1, 2, 6, 24, 120, . . .   7. _____
   A. 240   **B.** 720   **C.** 2,400   **D.** 600

8. Express 2.15 as a mixed number in simplest form.   8. _____
   A. $\frac{43}{25}$ **B.** $\frac{20}{41}$ **C.** $2\frac{3}{20}$ **D.** $\frac{215}{100}$

9. How many numbers are in the sequence 3, 6, 9, 12, . . . whose last number is 75?   9. _____
   A. 20   **B.** 15   **C.** 30   **D.** 25

10. Find the perimeter of a square whose side is $1\frac{2}{3}$ yards.   10. _____
    A. $6\frac{2}{3}$ yd   **B.** $7\frac{1}{3}$ yd   **C.** $8\frac{2}{3}$ **D.** $2\frac{7}{9}$

11. Add $2\frac{3}{8}$ and $1\frac{7}{24}$. Write the answer in simplest form.   11. _____
    A. $2\frac{2}{3}$ **B.** $3\frac{1}{3}$ **C.** $4\frac{1}{3}$ **D.** $3\frac{2}{3}$

12. Subtract $1\frac{3}{4}$ from $4\frac{1}{9}$. Write the answer in simplest form.   12. _____
    A. $3\frac{13}{36}$ **B.** $3\frac{2}{5}$ **C.** $2\frac{13}{36}$ **D.** $2\frac{2}{5}$

13. Find the area of the rectangle: $l = 5.6$ meters and $w = 0.7$ meters.   13. _____
    A. 7.84 m^2 **B.** 3.92 m^2 **C.** 6.3 m^2 **D.** 4 m^2

14. Translate *the sum of p and 5* into an algebraic expression.   14. _____
    A. $p + 5$ **B.** $5p$ **C.** $p \div 5$ **D.** $p - 5$

15. Convert 1.75 pounds to ounces.   15. _____
    A. 20   **B.** 24   **C.** 28   **D.** 18

16. Write 8×10^{-3} in standard form.   16. _____
    A. 8,000   **B.** 800   **C.** 0.008   **D.** 0.0008

Solve each equation.

17. $\frac{8}{9} - \frac{5}{6} = r$ **A.** $\frac{1}{18}$ **B.** 1   **C.** $\frac{1}{9}$ **D.** $\frac{1}{6}$ 17. _____

18. $-3s = 1.2$ **A.** 0.04   **B.** -0.04   **C.** -0.4   **D.** 0.4   18. _____

19. $t - 7 = -15$ **A.** -22   **B.** -8   **C.** 8   **D.** 22   19. _____

20. $-10 = -5 + m$ **A.** -15   **B.** 2   **C.** -5   **D.** 50   20. _____

Form 1A

Chapter 8 Test

1. The measure of an angle is 45°. Classify the angle.   1. _____
   A. acute   **B.** straight   **C.** obtuse   **D.** right

2. The measure of an angle is 180°. Classify the angle.   2. _____
   A. acute   **B.** straight   **C.** obtuse   **D.** right

3. The measure of an angle is 135°. Classify the angle.   3. _____
   A. acute   **B.** straight   **C.** obtuse   **D.** right

4. Which figure is a polygon?   4. _____
   A. △   **B.** ⊔   **C.** ○   **D.** ⊔⊓

5. Which figure is *not* a polygon?   5. _____
   A. ▭   **B.** ⬡   **C.** □   **D.** ⊠

6. Classify a polygon having eight sides.   6. _____
   A. hexagon   **B.** heptagon   **C.** octagon   **D.** decagon

7. Classify triangle *X* by its sides and by its angles.   7. _____
   A. scalene, obtuse   **B.** scalene, right
   C. isosceles, right   **D.** scalene, acute

8. Classify triangle *Y* by its sides and by its angles.   8. _____
   A. equilateral, acute   **B.** isosceles, obtuse
   C. equilateral, right   **D.** equilateral, obtuse

9. Classify triangle *Z* by its sides and by its angles.   9. _____
   A. isosceles, right   **B.** isosceles, obtuse
   C. isosceles, acute   **D.** equilateral, acute

Use quadrilaterals J and K below for Exercises 10 and 11. Let P = parallelogram, R = rectangle, S = square, RH = rhombus, and T = trapezoid. Which letters describe each quadrilateral?

10. Quadrilateral *J*   10. _____
    A. P   **B.** P, RH   **C.** R   **D.** S, RH

11. Quadrilateral *K*   11. _____
    A. S, P   **B.** S, RH   **C.** S, R   **D.** P, R, S, RH

12. Which quadrilateral does *not* have two pairs of parallel sides?   12. _____
    A. trapezoid   **B.** rectangle   **C.** rhombus   **D.** square

Chapter 8 Test Form 1A (continued)

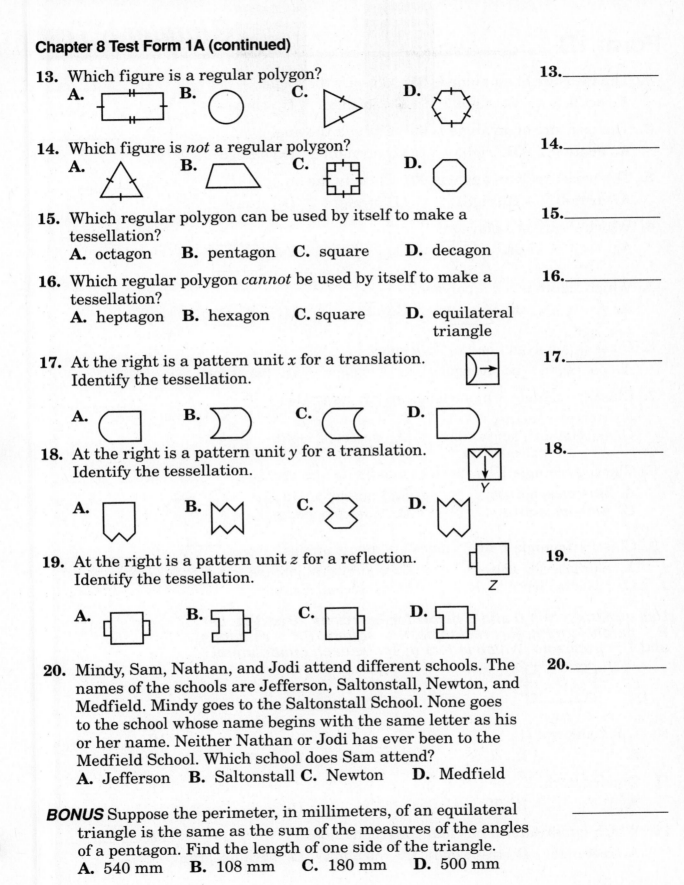

13. Which figure is a regular polygon?

   A.   B.   C.   D.

13._____

14. Which figure is *not* a regular polygon?

   A.   B.   C.   D.

14._____

15. Which regular polygon can be used by itself to make a tessellation?

   A. octagon   **B.** pentagon   **C.** square   **D.** decagon

15._____

16. Which regular polygon *cannot* be used by itself to make a tessellation?

   A. heptagon   **B.** hexagon   **C.** square   **D.** equilateral triangle

16._____

17. At the right is a pattern unit *x* for a translation. Identify the tessellation.

   A.   **B.**   **C.**   **D.**

17._____

18. At the right is a pattern unit *y* for a translation. Identify the tessellation.

   A.   **B.**   **C.**   **D.**

18._____

19. At the right is a pattern unit *z* for a reflection. Identify the tessellation.

   A.   **B.**   **C.**   **D.**

19._____

20. Mindy, Sam, Nathan, and Jodi attend different schools. The names of the schools are Jefferson, Saltonstall, Newton, and Medfield. Mindy goes to the Saltonstall School. None goes to the school whose name begins with the same letter as his or her name. Neither Nathan or Jodi has ever been to the Medfield School. Which school does Sam attend?
   A. Jefferson   **B.** Saltonstall **C.** Newton   **D.** Medfield

20._____

BONUS Suppose the perimeter, in millimeters, of an equilateral triangle is the same as the sum of the measures of the angles of a pentagon. Find the length of one side of the triangle.
   A. 540 mm   **B.** 108 mm   **C.** 180 mm   **D.** 500 mm

_____

Form 1B

1. The measure of an angle is 95°. Classify the angle.   1. _____
   A. acute   **B.** right   **C.** straight   **D.** obtuse

2. The measure of an angle is 60°. Classify the angle.   2. _____
   A. acute   **B.** right   **C.** straight   **D.** obtuse

3. The measure of an angle is 90°. Classify the angle.   3. _____
   A. acute   **B.** right   **C.** straight   **D.** obtuse

4. Which figure is a polygon?   4. _____
   A.   **B.**   **C.**   **D.**

5. Which figure is *not* a polygon?   5. _____
   A.   **B.**   **C.**   **D.**

6. Classify a polygon having five sides.   6. _____
   A. pentagon   **B.** decagon   **C.** hexagon   **D.** heptagon

7. Classify triangle *X* by its sides and by its angles.   7. _____
   A. isosceles, acute   **B.** scalene, right
   C. equilateral, acute   **D.** isosceles, right

8. Classify triangle *Y* by its sides and by its angles.   8. _____
   A. isosceles, obtuse   **B.** scalene, acute
   C. scalene, obtuse   **D.** isosceles, acute

9. Classify triangle *Z* by its sides and by its angles.   9. _____
   A. equilateral, acute   **B.** equilateral, obtuse
   C. scalene, acute   **D.** isosceles, right

Use quadrilaterals D and E below for Exercises 10 and 11. Let
P = parallelogram, R = rectangle, S = square, RH = rhombus,
and T = trapezoid. Which letters describe each quadrilateral?

10. Quadrilateral *D*   10. _____
    A. T   **B.** R, S   **C.** R, RH   **D.** P, R

11. Quadrilateral *E*   11. _____
    A. P   **B.** T   **C.** P, T   **D.** S, T

12. Which quadrilateral has four congruent sides?   12. _____
    A. rectangle   **B.** trapezoid   **C.** rhombus   **D.** parallelogram

Chapter 8 Test Form 1B (continued)

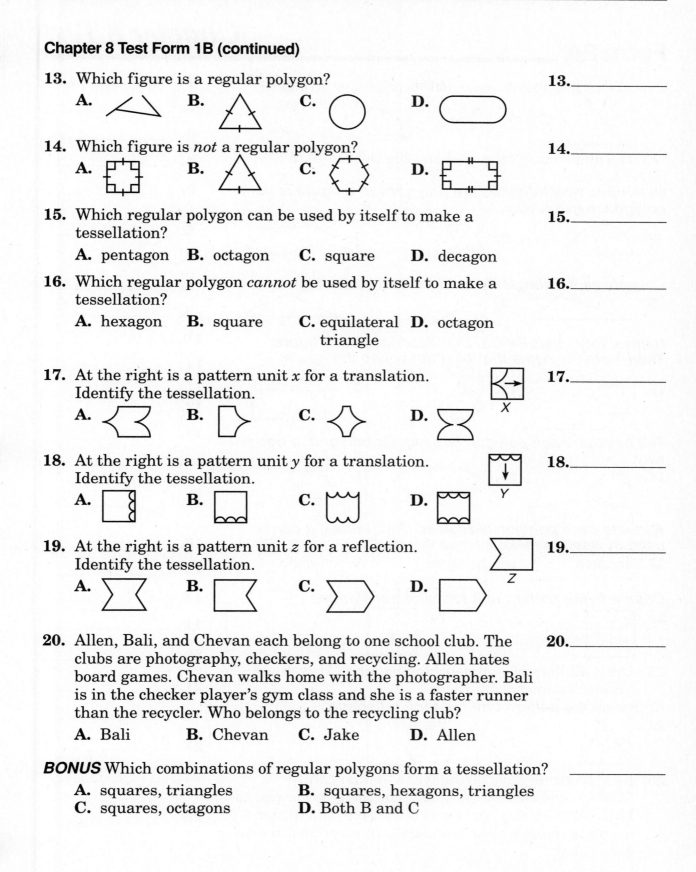

13. Which figure is a regular polygon?   13._____

    A.   **B.**   **C.**   **D.**

14. Which figure is *not* a regular polygon?   14._____

    A.   **B.**   **C.**   **D.**

15. Which regular polygon can be used by itself to make a tessellation?   15._____

    A. pentagon   **B.** octagon   **C.** square   **D.** decagon

16. Which regular polygon *cannot* be used by itself to make a tessellation?   16._____

    A. hexagon   **B.** square   **C.** equilateral triangle   **D.** octagon

17. At the right is a pattern unit x for a translation. Identify the tessellation.   17._____

    A.   **B.**   **C.**   **D.**

18. At the right is a pattern unit y for a translation. Identify the tessellation.   18._____

    A.   **B.**   **C.**   **D.**

19. At the right is a pattern unit z for a reflection. Identify the tessellation.   19._____

    A.   **B.**   **C.**   **D.**

20. Allen, Bali, and Chevan each belong to one school club. The clubs are photography, checkers, and recycling. Allen hates board games. Chevan walks home with the photographer. Bali is in the checker player's gym class and she is a faster runner than the recycler. Who belongs to the recycling club?   20._____

    A. Bali   **B.** Chevan   **C.** Jake   **D.** Allen

BONUS Which combinations of regular polygons form a tessellation?   _____

    A. squares, triangles   **B.** squares, hexagons, triangles
    C. squares, octagons   **D.** Both B and C

Form 2A _____

Chapter 8 Test

Classify each angle as acute, obtuse, right, or straight.

1.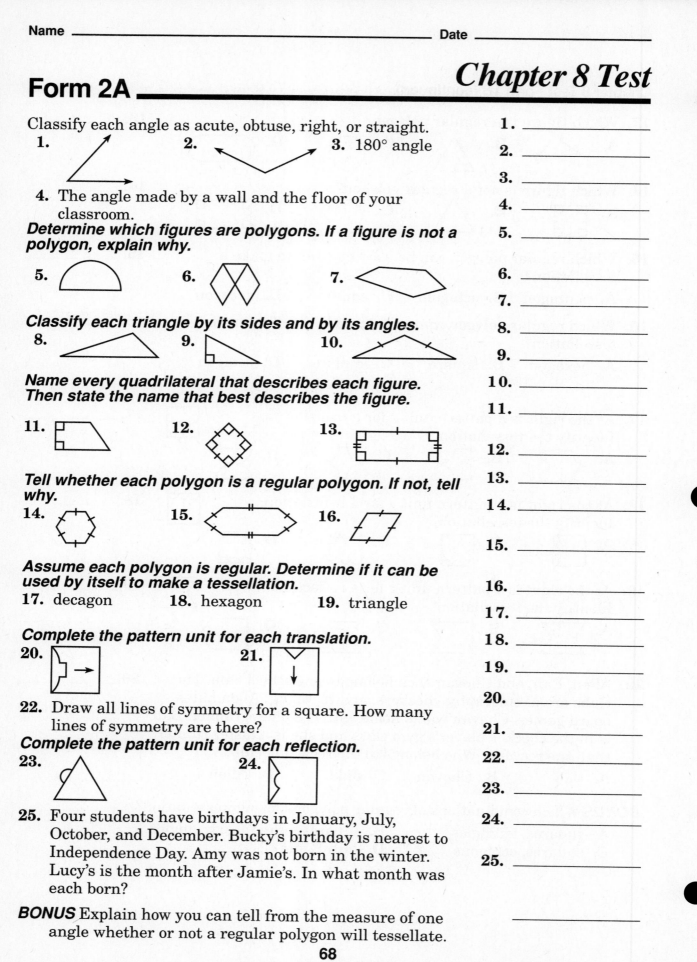

2.

3. 180° angle

4. The angle made by a wall and the floor of your classroom.

Determine which figures are polygons. If a figure is not a polygon, explain why.

5.

6.

7.

Classify each triangle by its sides and by its angles.

8.

9.

10.

Name every quadrilateral that describes each figure. Then state the name that best describes the figure.

11.

12.

13.

Tell whether each polygon is a regular polygon. If not, tell why.

14.

15.

16.

Assume each polygon is regular. Determine if it can be used by itself to make a tessellation.

17. decagon

18. hexagon

19. triangle

Complete the pattern unit for each translation.

20.

21.

22. Draw all lines of symmetry for a square. How many lines of symmetry are there?

Complete the pattern unit for each reflection.

23.

24.

25. Four students have birthdays in January, July, October, and December. Bucky's birthday is nearest to Independence Day. Amy was not born in the winter. Lucy's is the month after Jamie's. In what month was each born?

BONUS Explain how you can tell from the measure of one angle whether or not a regular polygon will tessellate.

1. _____
2. _____
3. _____
4. _____
5. _____
6. _____
7. _____
8. _____
9. _____
10. _____
11. _____
12. _____
13. _____
14. _____
15. _____
16. _____
17. _____
18. _____
19. _____
20. _____
21. _____
22. _____
23. _____
24. _____
25. _____

_____

Form 2B _____ *Chapter 8 Test*

Classify each angle as acute, obtuse, right, or straight.

1. 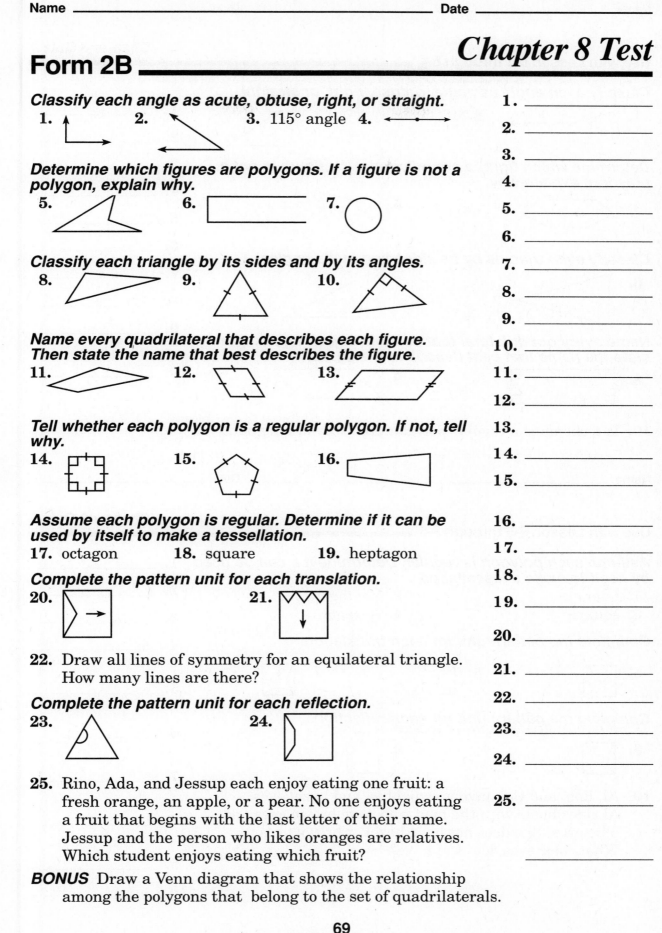 2. 3. 115° angle 4.

Determine which figures are polygons. If a figure is not a polygon, explain why.

5. 6. 7.

Classify each triangle by its sides and by its angles.

8. 9. 10.

Name every quadrilateral that describes each figure. Then state the name that best describes the figure.

11. 12. 13.

Tell whether each polygon is a regular polygon. If not, tell why.

14. 15. 16.

Assume each polygon is regular. Determine if it can be used by itself to make a tessellation.

17. octagon 18. square 19. heptagon

Complete the pattern unit for each translation.

20. 21.

22. Draw all lines of symmetry for an equilateral triangle. How many lines are there?

Complete the pattern unit for each reflection.

23. 24.

25. Rino, Ada, and Jessup each enjoy eating one fruit: a fresh orange, an apple, or a pear. No one enjoys eating a fruit that begins with the last letter of their name. Jessup and the person who likes oranges are relatives. Which student enjoys eating which fruit?

BONUS Draw a Venn diagram that shows the relationship among the polygons that belong to the set of quadrilaterals.

1. _____
2. _____
3. _____
4. _____
5. _____
6. _____
7. _____
8. _____
9. _____
10. _____
11. _____
12. _____
13. _____
14. _____
15. _____
16. _____
17. _____
18. _____
19. _____
20. _____
21. _____
22. _____
23. _____
24. _____
25. _____

Name _____ Date _____

Classify each angle as acute, obtuse, right, or straight.

1.   2. 180° angle   3.

Determine which figures are polygons. If a figure is not a polygon, explain why.

4.   5.

Classify each triangle by its sides and by its angles.

6.   7.

Name every quadrilateral that describes each figure. Then state the name that best describes the figure.

8.   9.

10. Is a rhombus a regular polygon? Tell why or why not.

1. _____
2. _____
3. _____
4. _____
5. _____
6. _____
7. _____
8. _____
9. _____
10. _____

- -

Name _____ Date _____

Assume each polygon is regular. Determine if it can be used by itself to make a tessellation.

1. triangle
3. square
2. pentagon
4. hexagon

Complete the pattern unit for each translation.

5.   6.   7.

Complete the pattern unit for each reflection.

8.   9.

10. Al, Bob, and Cal have brown, blue, and hazel eyes. Al rides home with the men who have brown eyes and blue eyes. Bob does not have hazel or brown eyes. What color eyes does Cal have?

1. _____
2. _____
3. _____
4. _____
5. _____
6. _____
7. _____
8. _____
9. _____
10. _____

Name _____ Date _____

Cumulative Review Chapters 1-8

1. Evaluate $(84 - 16) \div 4 + 13 \cdot 2$. (Lesson 1-7)
2. Change 1.87×10^5 to standard form. (Lesson 2-6)
3. Find the median of 55, 49, 54, 49, 50, 48, and 52. (Lesson 3-5)
4. Find the mean of 30, 25, 18, 20, 22, and 19. (Lesson 3-5)
5. Identify the sequence 3, 9, 27, 81, . . . as arithmetic, geometric, or neither. Then find the next three terms of the sequence. (Lesson 4-3)
6. Express $\frac{5}{9}$ as a decimal. (Lesson 4-7)
7. Find the GCF and LCM of 18 and 63. (Lessons 4-5, 4-9)
8. Find the perimeter of a rectangle with $l = 5\frac{5}{6}$ yd and $w = 2\frac{1}{6}$ yd. (Lesson 5-6)
9. Translate *twelve more than z* into an algebraic expression. (Lesson 6-4)
10. Find the area of the parallelogram with $b = 6$ mi and $h = 2.25$ mi. (Lesson 6-7)
11. Complete the pattern: 100, 97, 91, __?__, 70, 55, __?__. (Lesson 7-6)
12. Write an equation for the following: The quotient of a number r and 0.5 is -0.76. Then solve. (Lesson 7-9)

Solve each equation. Check your solution. (Lessons 5-3, 5-10, 6-3, 7-10)

13. $6\frac{3}{8} + 3\frac{1}{6} = a$
14. $8\frac{1}{8} - 2\frac{7}{10} = b$
15. $2\frac{2}{5} \div \frac{3}{10} = c$
16. $6\frac{1}{4} = d - 2\frac{1}{6}$
17. $e + 6.9 = 14.4$
18. $-171 = 3f$
19. $-145 = g + 67$
20. $\frac{h}{-4} = -89$
21. Classify a 75° angle as acute, obtuse, right, or straight. (Lesson 8-1)

Classify each triangle by its sides and by its angles. (Lesson 8-3)

22.

23.

Name every quadrilateral that describes each figure. Then state the name that best describes the figure. (Lesson 8-3)

24.

25.

1. _____
2. _____
3. _____
4. _____
5. _____
6. _____
7. _____
8. _____
9. _____
10. _____
11. _____
12. _____
13. _____
14. _____
15. _____
16. _____
17. _____
18. _____
19. _____
20. _____
21. _____
22. _____
23. _____
24. _____
25. _____

Glencoe Division, Macmillan/McGraw-Hill

Cumulative Test Chapters 1-8

1. Evaluate $(22 + 66) \div 4 + 4 \cdot 9$.   1. _____
   A. 58   B. 99   C. $\frac{11}{9}$ D. $\frac{9}{11}$

2. Change 7,930,000 to scientific notation.   2. _____
   A. 0.793×10^6 B. 7.93×10^5
   C. 7.93×10^6 D. 79.3×10^5

3. Find the median of 12, 36, 16, 30, and 24.   3. _____
   A. 25   B. 36   C. 23.6   D. 24

4. Find the mean of 80, 85, 90, 95, and 85.   4. _____
   A. 15   B. 87   C. 85   D. 95

5. Express $\frac{9}{11}$ as a decimal.   5. _____
   A. 0.8   B. 0.81   C. $0.\overline{81}$ D. $0.8\overline{1}$

6. Find the GCF and LCM of 28 and 84.   6. _____
   A. 28; 84   B. 7; 28   C. 84; 28   D. 14; 84

7. Find the perimeter of a rectangle with $l = 3\frac{3}{8}$ in. and   7. _____
   $w = 1\frac{3}{4}$ in.
   A. $10\frac{1}{4}$ in.   B. $5\frac{1}{8}$ in.   C. 5.9 in.   D. 6.0 in.

8. Find the area of the parallelogram with $b = 8.2$ m and   8. _____
   $h = 6.5$ m.
   A. 29.4 m^2 B. 14.7 m^2 C. 15 m^2 D. 53.3 m^2

9. Complete the pattern: 98, 100, 103, 107, _?_, _?_ .   9. _____
   A. 111, 119   B. 109, 115   C. 112, 118   D. 110, 116

10. Translate *the difference of x and 6* into an algebraic expression.   10. _____
    A. $x + 6$ B. $6x$ C. $x - 6$ D. $6 - x$

Solve each equation. Check your solution.

11. $6\frac{5}{8} - 3\frac{5}{6} = a$ A. $3\frac{19}{24}$ B. 3   C. $3\frac{1}{2}$ D. $2\frac{19}{24}$ 11. _____

12. $5\frac{1}{4} \div 2\frac{1}{2} = b$ A. $3\frac{1}{4}$ B. $13\frac{1}{8}$ C. $2\frac{1}{10}$ D. $3\frac{1}{4}$ 12. _____

13. $5\frac{2}{3} = c + 2\frac{1}{3}$ A. $3\frac{1}{3}$ B. 8   C. $3\frac{2}{3}$ D. $2\frac{2}{5}$ 13. _____

14. $d - 7.8 = 18.3$ A. 10.5   B. 26.1   C. 2   D. -10.5   14. _____

15. $-116 = 4f$ A. -29   B. -464   C. -112   D. 28   15. _____

16. $\frac{e}{-5} = -78$ A. -390   B. 39   C. 390   D. 15.6   16. _____

17. The measure of an angle is 91°. Classify the angle.   17. _____
    A. acute   B. obtuse   C. straight   D. right

18. Classify triangle X by its sides and by its angles.   18. _____
    A. isosceles, right   B. isosceles, acute
    C. scalene, right   D. equilateral, acute

19. Which quadrilateral does *not* have two pairs of parallel sides?   19. _____
    A. square   B. trapezoid
    C. rhombus   D. parallelogram

20. Classify a polygon having six sides.   20. _____
    A. octagon   B. heptagon   C. decagon   D. hexagon

Form 1A

1. Carmine is the youngest of four sisters. Each sister is four years older than the next youngest sister. The combined ages of Carmine and her sisters is 68. How old is Carmine?

   A. 23   **B.** 15   **C.** 11   **D.** 12

   1. _____

2. Find 30^2.

   A. 450   **B.** 30   **C.** 300   **D.** 900

   2. _____

3. Find $\sqrt{196}$.

   A. 14   **B.** 98   **C.** 49   **D.** 16

   3. _____

4. Which number is not a perfect square?

   A. 100   **B.** 200   **C.** 400   **D.** 2,500

   4. _____

5. Estimate $\sqrt{23}$.

   A. 4   **B.** 11   **C.** 6   **D.** 5

   5. _____

6. Estimate $\sqrt{102}$.

   A. 10   **B.** 11   **C.** 12   **D.** 10,404

   6. _____

7. Estimate $\sqrt{520}$.

   A. 20   **B.** 22   **C.** 23   **D.** 24

   7. _____

8. The lengths of the legs of a right triangle are 8 centimeters and 6 centimeters. Which equation would you solve to find the length of the hypotenuse?

   A. $6^2 + x^2 = 8^2$ **B.** $8^2 + x^2 = 6^2$
   C. $6^2 + 8^2 = x^2$ **D.** $8^2 - 6^2 = x^2$

   8. _____

9. The length of the hypotenuse of a right triangle is 20 feet and the length of one leg is 16 feet. Find the length of the other leg.

   A. 12 ft   **B.** 72 ft   **C.** 26 ft   **D.** 36 ft

   9. _____

10. Which could be the lengths of the sides of a right triangle?

    A. 6 m, 8 m, 9 m   **B.** 11 ft, 12 ft, 14 ft
    C. 30 cm, 40 cm, 50 cm   **D.** 3 cm, 4 cm, 7 cm

    10. _____

11. A 41-foot guy wire is used to brace an antenna. The wire is anchored 9 feet from the base of the antenna. How tall is the antenna?

    A. 42 ft   **B.** 40 ft   **C.** 80 ft   **D.** 22 ft

    11. _____

12. The Garcias drove 24 miles east and then 7 miles north. At that point, what is the straight-line distance from their starting point?

    A. 31 miles   **B.** 625 miles   **C.** 312.5 miles   **D.** 25 miles

    12. _____

Chapter 9 Test Form 1A continued

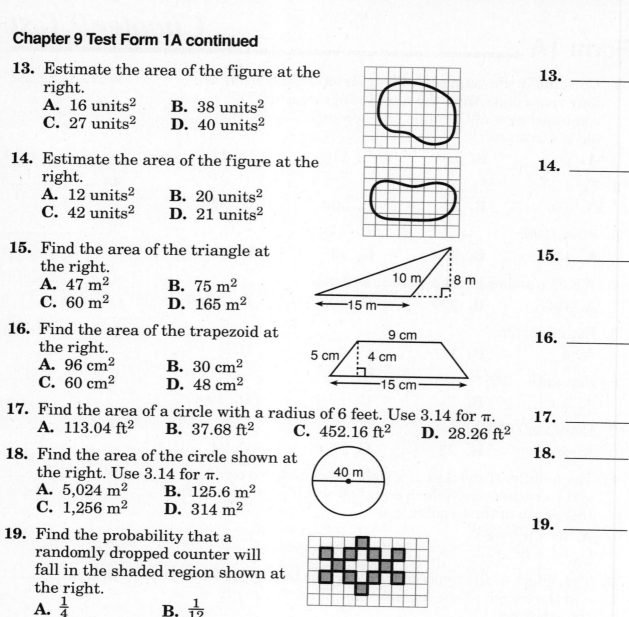

13. Estimate the area of the figure at the right.
   A. 16 units²   **B.** 38 units²
   C. 27 units²   **D.** 40 units²

13. _____

14. Estimate the area of the figure at the right.
   A. 12 units²   **B.** 20 units²
   C. 42 units²   **D.** 21 units²

14. _____

15. Find the area of the triangle at the right.
   A. 47 m²   **B.** 75 m²
   C. 60 m²   **D.** 165 m²

15. _____

16. Find the area of the trapezoid at the right.
   A. 96 cm²   **B.** 30 cm²
   C. 60 cm²   **D.** 48 cm²

16. _____

17. Find the area of a circle with a radius of 6 feet. Use 3.14 for π.
   A. 113.04 ft²   **B.** 37.68 ft²   **C.** 452.16 ft²   **D.** 28.26 ft²

17. _____

18. Find the area of the circle shown at the right. Use 3.14 for π.
   A. 5,024 m²   **B.** 125.6 m²
   C. 1,256 m²   **D.** 314 m²

18. _____

19. Find the probability that a randomly dropped counter will fall in the shaded region shown at the right.
   A. $\frac{1}{4}$ **B.** $\frac{1}{12}$
   C. $\frac{1}{5}$ **D.** $\frac{5}{1}$

19. _____

20. Find the probability that a randomly dropped counter will fall in the shaded region shown at the right.
   A. $\frac{4}{15}$ **B.** $\frac{4}{11}$
   C. $\frac{1}{16}$ **D.** $\frac{15}{4}$

20. _____

BONUS Find the length of $\overline{AB}$ in the cardboard box shown at the right. Round your answer to the nearest whole number.
   A. 10 in.   **B.** 82 in.
   C. 13 in.   **D.** 22 in.

_____

Form 1B

Chapter 9 Test

1. Pens are sold in packages of 5 and packages of 8. Jill bought a total of 39 pens. How many 5-pen packages did she buy?

   A. 3 packages   **B.** 0 packages   **C.** 5 packages   **D.** 8 packages

   1. _____

2. Find 18^2.

   A. 17   **B.** 162   **C.** 18   **D.** 324

   2. _____

3. Find $\sqrt{2{,}500}$.

   A. 50   **B.** 500   **C.** 1,250   **D.** 250

   3. _____

4. Which number is not a perfect square?

   A. 81   **B.** 121   **C.** 150   **D.** 144

   4. _____

5. Estimate $\sqrt{37}$.

   A. 18   **B.** 19   **C.** 7   **D.** 6

   5. _____

6. Estimate $\sqrt{143}$.

   A. 10   **B.** 11   **C.** 12   **D.** 20,499

   6. _____

7. Estimate $\sqrt{899}$.

   A. 20   **B.** 29   **C.** 30   **D.** 31

   7. _____

8. The lengths of the legs of a right triangle are 16 feet and 30 feet. Which equation would you solve to find the length of the hypotenuse?

   A. $16^2 + x^2 = 30$ **B.** $16^2 + 30^2 = x^2$
   C. $30^2 + x^2 = 16$ **D.** $30^2 - 16^2 = x^2$

   8. _____

9. The length of one leg of a right triangle is 24 meters and the length of the hypotenuse is 25 meters. Find the length of the other leg.

   A. 7 m   **B.** 35 m   **C.** 49 m   **D.** 1

   9. _____

10. Which could be the lengths of the sides of a right triangle?

    A. 7 cm, 8 cm, 10 cm   **B.** 20 m, 30 m, 40 m
    C. 12 ft, 15 ft, 20 ft   **D.** 6 cm, 8 cm, 10 cm

    10. _____

11. A rectangular picture frame is 24 inches long by 18 inches wide. A diagonal brace is nailed across the back of the frame. How long is the brace?

    A. 30 inches   **B.** 42 inches   **C.** 45 inches   **D.** 21 inches

    11. _____

12. A 52-foot cable reaches from the top of a pole to a point on the ground that is 48 feet from the base of the pole. How tall is the pole?

    A. 12 ft   **B.** 20 ft
    C. 92 ft   **D.** 50 ft

    52 ft   48 ft

    12. _____

Chapter 9 Test Form 1B continued

13. Estimate the area of the figure at the right.
    A. 28 units^2 **B.** 17 units^2
    C. 39 units^2 **D.** 32 units^2

13. _____

14. Estimate the area of the figure at the right.
    A. 8 units^2 **B.** 29 units^2
    C. 20 units^2 **D.** 30 units^2

14. _____

15. Find the area of the triangle at the right.
    A. 225 m^2 **B.** 360 m^2
    C. 180 m^2 **D.** 90 m^2

15. _____

16. Find the area of the trapezoid at the right.
    A. 348 mm^2 **B.** 588 mm^2
    C. 735 mm^2 **D.** 294 mm^2

16. _____

17. Find the area of a circle with a diameter of 24 ft. Use 3.14 for π.
    A. 1,808.64 ft^2 **B.** 37.68 ft^2 **C.** 452.16 ft^2 **D.** 7,234 ft^2

17. _____

18. Find the area of the circle shown at the right. Use 3.14 for π.
    A. 254.34 mm^2 **B.** 56.52 mm^2
    C. 1017.36 mm^2 **D.** 63.59 mm^2

18. _____

19. Find the probability that a randomly-dropped counter will fall in the shaded region shown at the right.
    A. $\frac{1}{8}$ **B.** $\frac{2}{15}$
    C. $\frac{2}{13}$ **D.** $\frac{15}{2}$

19. _____

20. Find the probability that a randomly-dropped counter will fall in the shaded region shown at the right.
    A. $\frac{1}{4}$ **B.** $\frac{1}{12}$
    C. $\frac{1}{5}$ **D.** $\frac{5}{1}$

20. _____

BONUS Find the length of $\overline{CD}$ in the cardboard box shown at the right. Round your answer to the nearest whole number.
    A. 500 cm   **B.** 250 cm
    C. 22 cm   **D.** 42 cm

_____

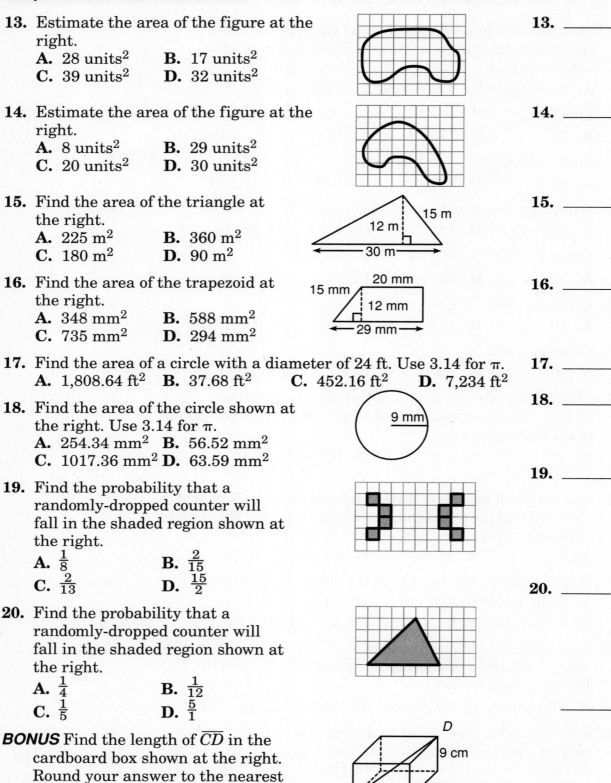

Glencoe Division, Macmillan/McGraw-Hill

Form 2A _____

1. The product of two numbers is 2,000. The difference of the two numbers is 10. What are the numbers?

Find the square root of each number. If it is not a perfect square, estimate to the nearest whole number.

2. $\sqrt{289}$ **3.** $\sqrt{196}$ **4.** $\sqrt{200}$

Find the square of each number.

5. 8   **6.** 15   **7.** 20

If the legs of a right triangle are a and b and the hypotenuse is c, find the missing length. Round decimal answers to the nearest tenth.

8. a: 12 m; b: 16 m   **9.** b: 24 cm; c: 30 cm

10. a: 5 ft; c: 8 ft

11. A 15-foot ladder is propped against a wall. The base of the ladder is 9 feet from the base of the wall. How far up the wall does the ladder reach?

12. Sally drives 10 miles east and then 10 miles south. At this point, what is the straight line distance from her starting point. Estimate to the nearest whole number.

Estimate the area of each figure.

13.   **14.**

Find the area of each triangle or trapezoid.

15.   **16.**
25 m 24 m 30 m   33 cm 20 cm 16 cm 57 cm

Find the area of each circle. Use 3.14 for π. Round answers to the nearest hundredth.

17. radius, 14 inches   **18.** diameter, 34 meters

Find the probability that a randomly-dropped counter will fall in the shaded region.

19.   **20.**

BONUS Find the area of the shaded region shown at the right.

10 mm

20 mm

1. _____

2. _____

3. _____

4. _____

5. _____

6. _____

7. _____

8. _____

9. _____

10. _____

11. _____

12. _____

13. _____

14. _____

15. _____

16. _____

17. _____

18. _____

19. _____

20. _____

Form 2B

1. The product of two consecutive even numbers is 960. What are the two numbers?

Find the square root of each number. If it is not a perfect square, estimate to the nearest whole number.

2. $\sqrt{256}$ 3. $\sqrt{441}$ 4. $\sqrt{120}$

Find the square of each number.

5. 12   6. 7   7. 40

If the legs of a right triangle are a and b and the hypotenuse is c, find the missing length. Round decimal answers to the nearest tenth.

8. a: 15 m; b: 20 m   9. a: 30 cm; c: 50 cm

10. b: 7 ft; c: 11 ft

11. A rectangular field is 80 meters long by 60 meters wide. What is the diagonal distance across the field?

12. A 25-foot cable is used to brace a ship mast. The cable is anchored 7 feet from the foot of the mast. How tall is the mast?

Estimate the area of each figure.

13.   14.

Find the area of each triangle or trapezoid.

15. 25 mm, 20 mm, 50 mm   16. 33 cm, 20 cm, 16 cm, 57 cm

Find the area of each circle. Use 3.14 for π.

17. radius, 18 cm   18. diameter, 42 inches

Find the probability that a randomly-dropped counter will fall in the shaded region.

19.   20.

BONUS Find the area of the shaded region at the right.

4 cm, 2 cm, 4 cm, 2 cm

1. _____
2. _____
3. _____
4. _____
5. _____
6. _____
7. _____
8. _____
9. _____
10. _____
11. _____
12. _____
13. _____
14. _____
15. _____
16. _____
17. _____
18. _____
19. _____
20. _____
_____

Glencoe Division, Macmillan/McGraw-Hill

Use with Lessons 9-1 through 9-5

1. Jobeth is thinking of two numbers. The sum of the numbers is 100. The difference of the numbers is 20. What are the numbers?

Find each square root.

2. $\sqrt{36}$　　　　**3.** $\sqrt{361}$　　　　**4.** $\sqrt{4,900}$

Estimate to the nearest whole number.

5. $\sqrt{63}$　　　　**6.** $\sqrt{150}$　　　　**7.** $\sqrt{223}$

Find the missing length. Round decimal answers to the nearest tenth.

8.

14 ft, c, 48 ft

9.

12 cm, 9 cm, a

10. A vertical pole is anchored to the ground by a 29-foot guy wire. The wire is attached to the ground at a point 21 feet from the base of the pole. How tall is the pole?

1. _____
2. _____
3. _____
4. _____
5. _____
6. _____
7. _____
8. _____
9. _____
10. _____

Use with Lessons 9-6 through 9-9

Estimate the area of each figure.

1.

2.

Find the area of each triangle or trapezoid.

3.

80 m, 64 m, 120 m

4.

60 mm, 65 mm, 80 mm

5.

20 ft, 30 ft, 18 ft, 68 ft

Find the area of each circle.

6. radius, 4 ft　　**7.** diameter, 38 m　　**8.**

3.6 m

Find the probability that a randomly-dropped counter will fall in the shaded region.

9.

10.

1. _____
2. _____
3. _____
4. _____
5. _____
6. _____
7. _____
8. _____
9. _____
10. _____

Cumulative Review Chapters 1-9

Evaluate. (Lessons 1-7, 1-9)

1. $(23 + 67) \div (12 - 2)$ **2.** 6^4

Multiply or divide. (Lessons 2-4, 2-7)

3. $0.012 \overline{)1.68}$ **4.** 0.0059×10^5

5. Write 870,000,000 in scientific notation. (Lesson 2-6)

6. Make a line plot for the data 36, 36, 36, 35, 33, 35, and 34 at the right. (Lesson 3-4)

Find the following for the data in Exercise 6. (Lessons 3-3, 3-5)

7. range   **8.** mode(s)

9. median   **10.** mean

11. Write the prime factorization of 120. (Lesson 4-2)

12. Find the GCF and LCM of 42 and 60. (Lessons 4-5, 4-9)

Solve each equation. Write each solution in simplest form. (Lessons 5-3, 5-10, 6-1, 6-3, 7-9)

13. $\frac{1}{24} + \frac{1}{8} = x$ **14.** $1\frac{5}{12} \div \frac{3}{4} = s$

15. $c - \frac{1}{3} = 3\frac{1}{5}$ **16.** $3.1m = 9.3$

17. $-10 = n - 4$ **18.** $\frac{y}{7} = -23$

19. How many pounds are in 4.5 tons? (Lesson 6-6)

20. Complete the pattern: 100, 96, 88, 76, __?__ . (Lesson 7-6)

21. Classify a 120° angle as acute, obtuse, right, or straight. (Lesson 8-1)

22. Classify the triangle below by its sides and by its angles. (Lesson 8-3)

23. Estimate $\sqrt{172}$. (Lesson 9-3)

24. The lengths of the legs of a right triangle are 14 feet and 48 feet. Find the length of the hypotenuse. (Lesson 9-4)

25. Find the area of a circle with a radius of 23 feet. (Lesson 9-8)

1. _____

2. _____

3. _____

4. _____

5. _____

6. _____

7. _____

8. _____

9. _____

10. _____

11. _____

12. _____

13. _____

14. _____

15. _____

16. _____

17. _____

18. _____

19. _____

20. _____

21. _____

22. _____

23. _____

24. _____

25. _____

Glencoe Division, Macmillan/McGraw-Hill

Cumulative Test Chapters 1-9

1. Evaluate 8^3. **A.** 24 **B.** 64 **C.** 512 **D.** 6,561   1. _____

Multiply or divide.

2. 0.0018×0.03. **A.** 0.0054 **B.** 0.000054 **C.** 0.54 **D.** 0.054   2. _____

3. $0.018\overline{)7.2}$ **A.** 4 **B.** 40 **C.** 0.04 **D.** 400   3. _____

4. Write 7,500,000,000,000 in scientific notation.   4. _____
   A. 7.5×10^{11} **B.** 7.5×10^{12} **C.** 75×10^{12} **D.** 7.5×10^{13}

Find the following for the data 60, 48, 58, 50, 60, 49, 53.

5. mode(s) **A.** 53 **B.** 54 **C.** 60 **D.** 12   5. _____

6. median **A.** 53 **B.** 54 **C.** 60 **D.** 12   6. _____

7. range **A.** 53 **B.** 54 **C.** 60 **D.** 12   7. _____

8. Find the prime factorization of 160.   8. _____
   A. $10 \cdot 16$ **B.** $2 \cdot 2 \cdot 2 \cdot 2 \cdot 5$
   C. $2 \cdot 2 \cdot 2 \cdot 2 \cdot 2 \cdot 5$ **D.** $5 \cdot 32$

9. Find the GCF and LCM of 18 and 24.   9. _____
   A. 6, 36 **B.** 6, 48 **C.** 6, 72 **D.** 6, 144

Solve each equation. Write each solution in simplest form.

10. $\frac{3}{20} + \frac{1}{4} = x$ **A.** $\frac{1}{6}$ **B.** $\frac{1}{5}$ **C.** $\frac{2}{5}$ **D.** 6   10. _____

11. $2\frac{5}{9} \div \frac{5}{9} = y$ **A.** $4\frac{3}{5}$ **B.** $\frac{5}{23}$ **C.** $\frac{45}{207}$ **D.** $1\frac{34}{81}$ 11. _____

12. $2.1m = 8.4$ **A.** 0.4 **B.** 4 **C.** 17.64 **D.** $\frac{1}{4}$ 12. _____

13. $\frac{s}{8} = -16$ **A.** 2 **B.** -2 **C.** -128 **D.** 128   13. _____

14. How many ounces are in 1.5 pounds?   14. _____
    A. 15 ounces **B.** 24 ounces **B.** 150 ounces **D.** 48 ounces

15. Complete the pattern: 100, 95, 85, __?__, 50, 25.   15. _____
    A. 75 **B.** 80 **C.** 70 **D.** 95

16. Classify a 179° angle as acute, obtuse, right, or straight.   16. _____
    A. acute **B.** obtuse **C.** right **D.** straight

17. Classify the triangle at the right by its sides and by its angles. 17. _____
    A. isosceles, acute **B.** isosceles, obtuse
    C. scalene, acute **D.** scalene, right

18. Estimate $\sqrt{97}$.   18. _____
    A. 9 **B.** 10 **C.** 11 **D.** 8

19. The lengths of the sides of a right triangle are 24 feet and   19. _____
    32 feet. Find the length of the hypotenuse.
    A. 56 ft **B.** 800 ft **C.** 28 ft **D.** 40 ft

20. Find the area of a circle with a 9-foot radius.   20. _____
    A. 254.34 ft^2 **B.** 28.26 ft^2
    C. 1,017.36 ft^2 **D.** 63.59 ft^2

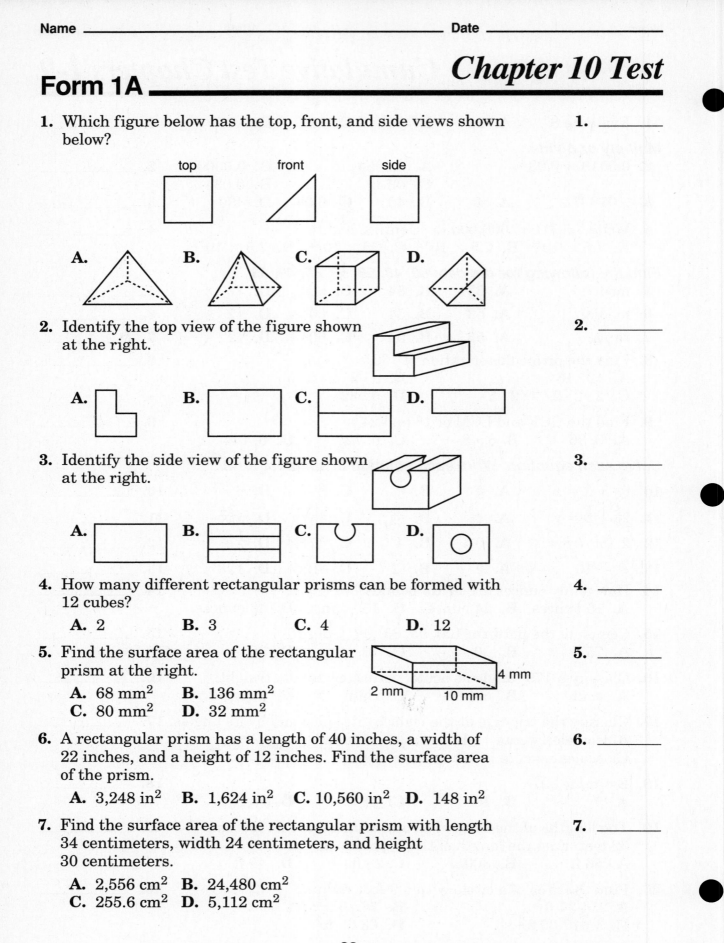

1. Which figure below has the top, front, and side views shown below?

1. _____

top   front   side

A.   B.   C.   D.

2. Identify the top view of the figure shown at the right.

2. _____

A.   B.   C.   D.

3. Identify the side view of the figure shown at the right.

3. _____

A.   B.   C.   D.

4. How many different rectangular prisms can be formed with 12 cubes?

4. _____

    A. 2   **B.** 3   **C.** 4   **D.** 12

5. Find the surface area of the rectangular prism at the right.

5. _____

4 mm 2 mm 10 mm

    A. 68 mm^2 **B.** 136 mm^2
    C. 80 mm^2 **D.** 32 mm^2

6. A rectangular prism has a length of 40 inches, a width of 22 inches, and a height of 12 inches. Find the surface area of the prism.

6. _____

    A. 3,248 in^2 **B.** 1,624 in^2 **C.** 10,560 in^2 **D.** 148 in^2

7. Find the surface area of the rectangular prism with length 34 centimeters, width 24 centimeters, and height 30 centimeters.

7. _____

    A. 2,556 cm^2 **B.** 24,480 cm^2
    C. 255.6 cm^2 **D.** 5,112 cm^2

Chapter 10 Test Form 1A (continued)

8. Find the surface area of the cylinder shown at the right. Use 3.14 for π.

A. 471 ft^2 B. 157 ft^2
C. 628 ft^2 D. 1,204 ft^2

8. _____

9. Find the surface area of a cylinder with a height of 19 centimeters and a base with a radius of 7 centimeters. Use 3.14 for π.

A. 1,142.96 cm^2 B. 307.72 cm^2
C. 2,923.34 cm^2 D. 614.72 cm^2

9. _____

10. Find the volume of the rectangular prism at the right.

A. 862 mm^3 B. 1,724 mm^3
C. 4,032 mm^3 D. 110 mm^3

10. _____

11. Find the volume of a rectangular prism with length 2.8 centimeters, width 1.5 centimeters, and height 1.2 centimeters.

A. 5.04 cm^3 B. 9.36 cm^3 C. 18.72 cm^3 D. 11 cm^3

11. _____

12. Find the volume of the cylinder at the right. Use $\frac{22}{7}$ for π.

A. 66 in^3 B. 77 in^3
C. 132 in^3 D. 462 in^3

12. _____

13. A can of juice is 6 inches high and its base has a radius of $1\frac{1}{2}$ inches. Find the volume of the can. Use $\frac{22}{7}$ for π.

A. $42\frac{3}{7}$ in^3 B. $28\frac{2}{7}$ in^3 C. $14\frac{1}{7}$ in^3 D. $\frac{22}{7}$ in^3

13. _____

14. A reflecting pool is 6 feet long by 4 feet wide by 6 inches deep. What is the volume of the pool?

A. 144 ft^3 B. 12 ft^3 C. 168 ft^3 D. 296 ft^3

14. _____

15. A tree is planted in a container shaped like a cylinder. The height of the container is 2 feet, and the radius of the base is 2 feet. Which formula could you use to find the volume of the container?

A. $V = lwh$
C. $A = 2\pi r^2 + 2\pi rh$ B. $V = \pi r^2 h$
     D. $A = 2(lh + lw + wh)$

15. _____

BONUS A cube has a volume of 1,000 cubic inches. What is the surface area of the cube?

A. 400 in^2 B. 600 in^2 C. 100 in^2 D. 6,000 in^2

_____

Form 1B

1. Which figure below has the top, front, and side views shown below?

1. _____

top   front   side

A.   **B.**   **C.**   **D.**

2. Identify the top view of the figure shown at the right.

2. _____

A.   **B.**   **C.**   **D.**

3. Identify the side view of the figure shown at the right.

3. _____

A.   **B.**   **C.**   **D.**

4. How many different rectangular prisms can be formed with 10 cubes?

4. _____

   A. 1   **B.** 2   **C.** 4   **D.** 10

5. Find the surface area of the rectangular prism at the right.

5. _____

5 cm
10 cm
25 cm

   A. 850 cm^2 **B.** 425 cm^2
   C. 1,250 cm^2 **D.** 80 cm^2

6. A rectangular prism has a length of 31 millimeters, a width of 28 millimeters, and a height of 15 millimeters. Find the surface area of the prism.

6. _____

   A. 1,753 mm^2 **B.** 13,020 mm^2
   C. 3,406 mm^2 **D.** 3,506 mm^2

7. Find the surface area of the rectangular prism with length 60 feet, width 42 feet, and height 31 feet.

7. _____

   A. 11,364 ft^2 **B.** 78,120 ft^2
   C. 134 ft^2 **D.** 266 ft^2

Chapter 10 Test Form 1B (continued)

8. Find the surface area of the cylinder shown at the right. Use 3.14 for π.

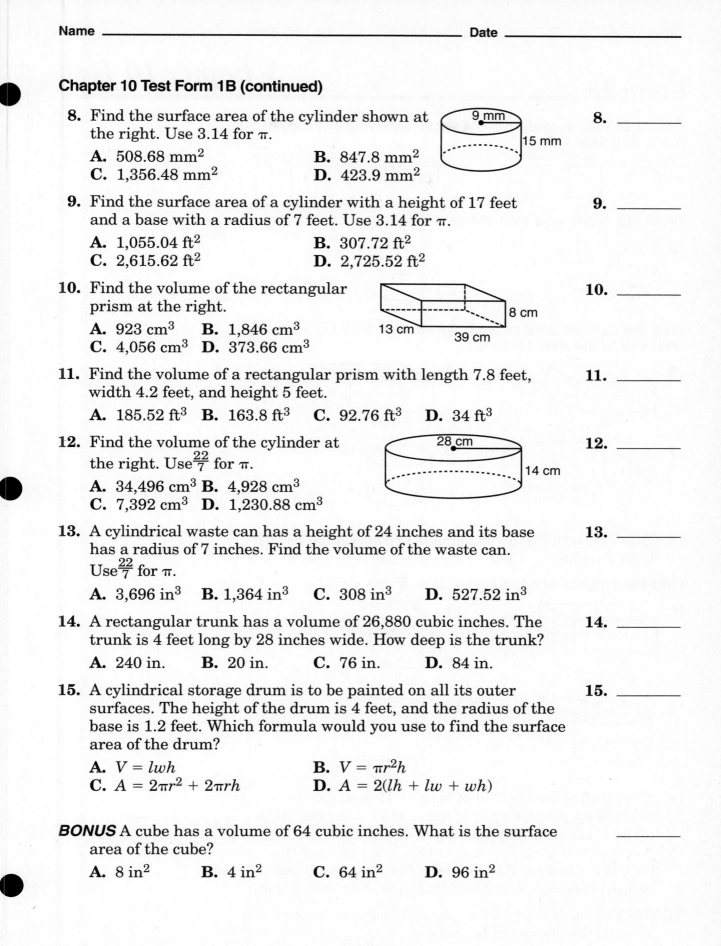

   A. 508.68 mm²   **B.** 847.8 mm²
   C. 1,356.48 mm²   **D.** 423.9 mm²

8. _____

9. Find the surface area of a cylinder with a height of 17 feet and a base with a radius of 7 feet. Use 3.14 for π.

   A. 1,055.04 ft²   **B.** 307.72 ft²
   C. 2,615.62 ft²   **D.** 2,725.52 ft²

9. _____

10. Find the volume of the rectangular prism at the right.

   A. 923 cm³   **B.** 1,846 cm³
   C. 4,056 cm³   **D.** 373.66 cm³

10. _____

11. Find the volume of a rectangular prism with length 7.8 feet, width 4.2 feet, and height 5 feet.

   A. 185.52 ft³   **B.** 163.8 ft³   **C.** 92.76 ft³   **D.** 34 ft³

11. _____

12. Find the volume of the cylinder at the right. Use $\frac{22}{7}$ for π.

   A. 34,496 cm³ **B.** 4,928 cm³
   C. 7,392 cm³   **D.** 1,230.88 cm³

12. _____

13. A cylindrical waste can has a height of 24 inches and its base has a radius of 7 inches. Find the volume of the waste can. Use $\frac{22}{7}$ for π.

   A. 3,696 in³   **B.** 1,364 in³   **C.** 308 in³   **D.** 527.52 in³

13. _____

14. A rectangular trunk has a volume of 26,880 cubic inches. The trunk is 4 feet long by 28 inches wide. How deep is the trunk?

   A. 240 in.   **B.** 20 in.   **C.** 76 in.   **D.** 84 in.

14. _____

15. A cylindrical storage drum is to be painted on all its outer surfaces. The height of the drum is 4 feet, and the radius of the base is 1.2 feet. Which formula would you use to find the surface area of the drum?

   A. $V = lwh$
   B. $V = \pi r^2 h$
   C. $A = 2\pi r^2 + 2\pi rh$
   D. $A = 2(lh + lw + wh)$

15. _____

BONUS A cube has a volume of 64 cubic inches. What is the surface area of the cube?

   A. 8 in²   **B.** 4 in²   **C.** 64 in²   **D.** 96 in²

_____

Form 2A _____   *Chapter 10 Test*

Draw each three-dimensional figure by using the top, front, and side views.

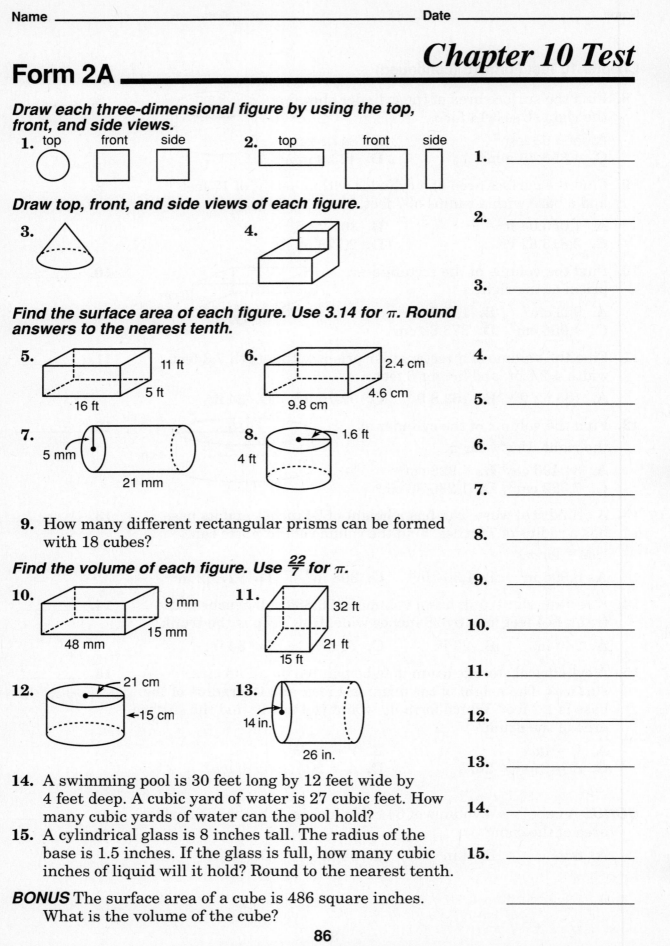

1. top   front   side

2. top   front   side

Draw top, front, and side views of each figure.

3.

4.

Find the surface area of each figure. Use 3.14 for π. Round answers to the nearest tenth.

5. 11 ft   5 ft   16 ft

6. 2.4 cm   4.6 cm   9.8 cm

7. 5 mm   21 mm

8. 1.6 ft   4 ft

9. How many different rectangular prisms can be formed with 18 cubes?

Find the volume of each figure. Use $\frac{22}{7}$ for π.

10. 9 mm   15 mm   48 mm

11. 32 ft   21 ft   15 ft

12. 21 cm   15 cm

13. 14 in.   26 in.

14. A swimming pool is 30 feet long by 12 feet wide by 4 feet deep. A cubic yard of water is 27 cubic feet. How many cubic yards of water can the pool hold?

15. A cylindrical glass is 8 inches tall. The radius of the base is 1.5 inches. If the glass is full, how many cubic inches of liquid will it hold? Round to the nearest tenth.

BONUS The surface area of a cube is 486 square inches. What is the volume of the cube?

1. _____

2. _____

3. _____

4. _____

5. _____

6. _____

7. _____

8. _____

9. _____

10. _____

11. _____

12. _____

13. _____

14. _____

15. _____

_____

Form 2B

Draw each three-dimensional figure by using the top, front, and side views.

1.   top   front   side 2. top   front   side

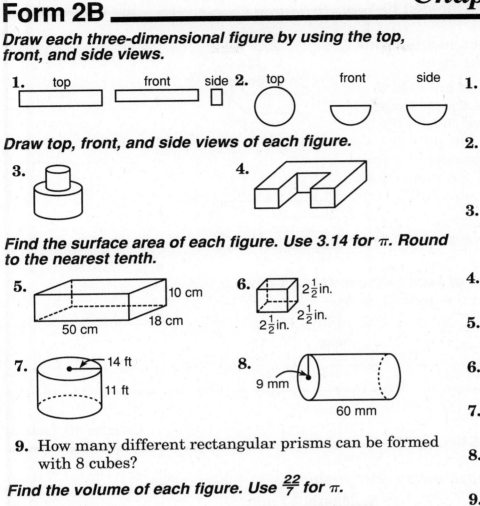

Draw top, front, and side views of each figure.

3.

4.

Find the surface area of each figure. Use 3.14 for π. Round to the nearest tenth.

5. 10 cm   18 cm   50 cm

6. $2\frac{1}{2}$ in. $2\frac{1}{2}$ in. $2\frac{1}{2}$ in.

7. 14 ft   11 ft

8. 9 mm   60 mm

9. How many different rectangular prisms can be formed with 8 cubes?

Find the volume of each figure. Use $\frac{22}{7}$ for π.

10. 24 cm   30 cm   56 cm

11. 7.5 in.   19.5 in.   48 in.

12. 35 mm   100 mm

13. 7 cm   7 cm

14. A storage shed with a flat roof is 4 yards long by 3 yards wide by $2\frac{1}{2}$ yards tall. A cubic yard is equal to 27 cubic feet. How many cubic feet of storage space does the shed enclose?

15. A cylindrical carton is covered with paper. The height of the carton is 9 inches and the radius of the base is 2 inches. What is the total surface area of the carton?

BONUS The surface area of a cube is 294 cm². What is the volume of the cube?

1. _____

2. _____

3. _____

4. _____

5. _____

6. _____

7. _____

8. _____

9. _____

10. _____

11. _____

12. _____

13. _____

14. _____

15. _____

_____

Name _____ Date _____

Use with Lessons 10-1 through 10-4 ▬▬▬▬▬▬▬▬

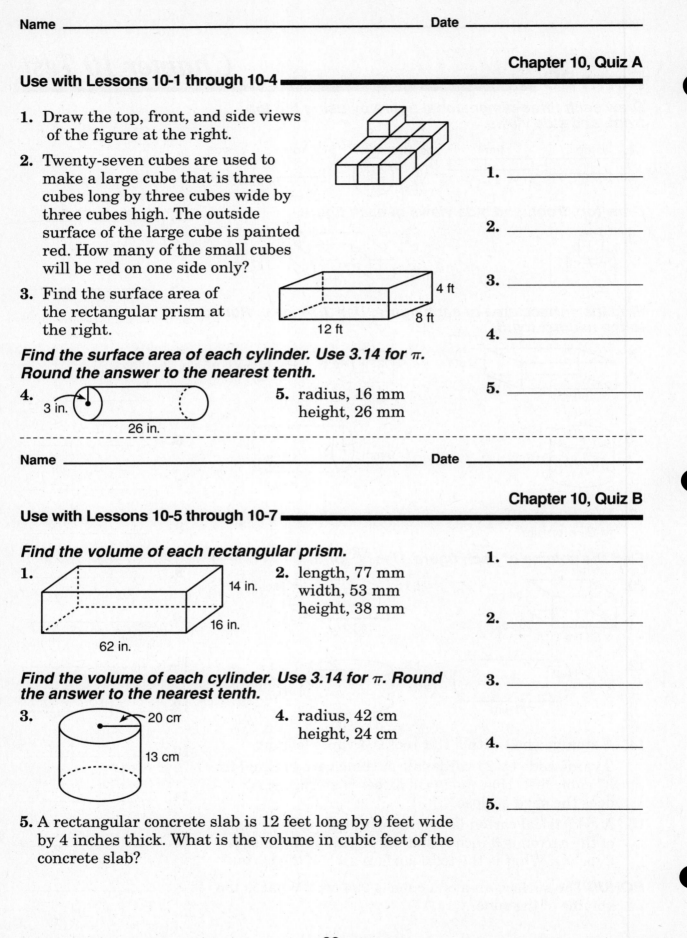

1. Draw the top, front, and side views of the figure at the right.

2. Twenty-seven cubes are used to make a large cube that is three cubes long by three cubes wide by three cubes high. The outside surface of the large cube is painted red. How many of the small cubes will be red on one side only?

3. Find the surface area of the rectangular prism at the right.

4 ft
8 ft
12 ft

Find the surface area of each cylinder. Use 3.14 for π. Round the answer to the nearest tenth.

4.
3 in.
26 in.

5. radius, 16 mm
   height, 26 mm

1. _____

2. _____

3. _____

4. _____

5. _____

- -

Name _____ Date _____

Use with Lessons 10-5 through 10-7 ▬▬▬▬▬▬▬▬

Find the volume of each rectangular prism.

1.
14 in.
16 in.
62 in.

2. length, 77 mm
   width, 53 mm
   height, 38 mm

Find the volume of each cylinder. Use 3.14 for π. Round the answer to the nearest tenth.

3.
20 cm
13 cm

4. radius, 42 cm
   height, 24 cm

5. A rectangular concrete slab is 12 feet long by 9 feet wide by 4 inches thick. What is the volume in cubic feet of the concrete slab?

1. _____

2. _____

3. _____

4. _____

5. _____

Glencoe Division, Macmillan/McGraw-Hill

Cumulative Review Chapters 1-10

1. Evaluate $3(x + y) - z$ if $x = 3$, $y = 7$, and $z = 8$. (Lesson 1-8)

2. Divide. $0.0007 \overline{)0.0000035}$ (Lesson 2-7)

3. Find the mean of 91, 88, 93, 82, and 91. (Lesson 3-5)

4. Express $\frac{5}{12}$ as a decimal. (Lesson 4-7)

5. How many pints are in 18 quarts? (Lesson 6-6)

Solve each equation. Write each solution in simplest form. (Lessons 5-3, 5-10, 6-3, 7-9)

6. $1\frac{3}{4} + 2\frac{1}{6} = x$

7. $5\frac{1}{10} - 2\frac{3}{5} = y$

8. $8\frac{1}{3} \div 1\frac{1}{9} = a$

9. $4\frac{3}{16} = x - 1\frac{1}{2}$

10. $g + 3.2 = 12.5$

11. $-108 = 9y$

12. $-100 = m + 32$

13. $\frac{s}{-3} = -27$

14. Classify a 70° angle as acute, obtuse, right, or straight. (Lesson 8-1)

15. Name every quadrilateral that describes the figure at the right. Then underline the name that best describes the figure. (Lesson 8-3)

16. The product of two consecutive even integers is 2,600. Find the two integers. (Lesson 9-1)

17. Estimate $\sqrt{403}$. (Lesson 9-3)

18. Determine if 16 meters, 20 meters, and 25 meters could be the lengths of the sides of a right triangle. (Lesson 9-4)

Find the area of each figure. (Lessons 6-7, 9-7, 9-8)

19. a parallelogram with a base of 14.5 feet and a height of 8.5 feet

20. a trapezoid with bases of 16 feet and 24 feet and a height of 12 feet

21. a circle with a radius of 15 feet (Use 3.14 for π.)

Refer to the figures at the right to find the following. Use 3.14 for π. Round answers to the nearest hundredth. (Lessons 10-3, 10-4, 10-5, 10-6)

22. surface area of the prism

23. surface area of the cylinder

24. volume of the prism

25. volume of the cylinder

50 mm
14 mm
43 mm

9 cm
18 cm

1. _____
2. _____
3. _____
4. _____
5. _____
6. _____
7. _____
8. _____
9. _____
10. _____
11. _____
12. _____
13. _____
14. _____
15. _____
16. _____
17. _____
18. _____
19. _____
20. _____
21. _____
22. _____
23. _____
24. _____
25. _____

Glencoe Division, Macmillan/McGraw-Hill

Cumulative Test Chapters 1-10

1. Evaluate $2(x + z) - y$ if $x = 10$, $y = 2$, and $z = 3$.   1. _____
   A. 21   **B.** 24   **C.** 22   **D.** 56

2. Divide: $0.00036 \div 0.004$ 2. _____
   A. 0.9   **B.** 0.009   **C.** 0.09   **D.** 0.009

3. Find the mean of 8, 12, 16, 8, 11, 15, 21.   3. _____
   A. 12   **B.** 13   **C.** 8   **D.** 9.2

4. Express $\frac{7}{9}$ as a decimal.   4. _____
   A. $0.\overline{7}$ **B.** 0.777   **C.** 0.077   **D.** $0.0\overline{7}$

5. How many pounds are in 3.5 tons?   5. _____
   A. 3,500   **B.** 350   **C.** 7,000   **D.** 8,000

Solve each equation. Write each solution in simplest form.

6. $6\frac{7}{24} - 2\frac{5}{8} = a$ **A.** $4\frac{1}{8}$ **B.** $4\frac{2}{3}$ **C.** $3\frac{2}{3}$ **D.** $3\frac{1}{3}$ 6. _____

7. $10\frac{2}{3} \div \frac{4}{9} = b$ **A.** $4\frac{20}{27}$ **B.** $\frac{27}{128}$ **C.** $\frac{1}{24}$ **D.** 24   7. _____

8. $-100 = 5y$ **A.** -20   **B.** 20   **C.** -500   **D.** 20   8. _____

9. $\frac{m}{-6} = -30$ **A.** -5   **B.** 5   **C.** 180   **D.** -180   9. _____

10. Which type of quadrilateral can never have four right angles?   10. _____
    A. rectangle   **B.** square   **C.** trapezoid   **D.** rhombus

11. Which could be the lengths of the sides of a right triangle?   11. _____
    A. 6 m, 8 m, 9 m   **B.** 10 cm, 24 cm, 26 cm
    C. 15 ft, 20 ft, 30 ft   **D.** 4 cm, 5 cm, 9 cm

12. Estimate $\sqrt{62}$.   12. _____
    A. 30   **B.** 8   **C.** 7   **D.** 3,844

13. Find the area of a trapezoid with bases of 34 feet and 16 feet and a height of 40 feet.   13. _____
    A. 2,000 ft^2 **B.** 1,000 ft^2 **C.** 200 ft^2 **D.** 544

14. Find the surface area of a rectangular prism with a length of 28 inches, a width of 12 inches, and a height of 20 inches.   14. _____
    A. 2,272 in^2 **B.** 1,136 in^2 **C.** 6,720 in^2 **D.** 120 in^2

15. Find the volume of a cylinder with a height of 30 centimeters and with a base having a radius of 10 centimeters. Use 3.14 for π.   15. _____
    A. 1,884 cm^3 **B.** 628 cm^3 **C.** 942 cm^3 **D.** 9,420 cm^3

Chapter 11 Test

Form 1A _____

1. Express the ratio 12 yards to 8 feet as a fraction in simplest form.   1. _____
   A. $\frac{12}{8}$ B. $\frac{3}{2}$ C. $\frac{1}{2}$ D. $\frac{9}{2}$

2. Express the rate of $1.35 for 45 pieces of paper as a unit rate.   2. _____
   A. 30¢ per piece   B. 0.03¢ per piece
   C. 3¢ per piece   D. 9¢ per piece

3. Solve the proportion $\frac{30}{42} = \frac{55}{d}$.   3. _____
   A. 39.3   B. 77   C. 67   D. 23

For Exercises 4 and 5, find the value of x in each pair of similar polygons.

4. A. 7 in.   B. 6.5 in.   4. _____
   C. 26 in.   D. 13 in.

   12 in. / 13 in. / 10 in.   6 in. / x in. / 5 in.

5. A. 1 ft   B. 3 ft   5. _____
   C. $\frac{3}{4}$ ft   D. $\frac{2}{3}$ ft

   x ft [6 ft   ]   4 ft / $\frac{1}{2}$ ft

6. On a map, the scale is 1 inch:125 miles. What is the actual   6. _____
   distance if the map distance is $4\frac{1}{2}$ inches?
   A. 525 miles   B. $562\frac{1}{2}$ miles C. $281\frac{1}{4}$ miles D. 505 miles

7. On a scale drawing, the scale is $\frac{1}{4}$ inch:1 foot. What are the   7. _____
   dimensions in the scale drawing for a room that is 15 feet
   by 24 feet?
   A. $3\frac{3}{4}$ inches by 6 inches   B. $7\frac{1}{2}$ inches by 12 inches
   C. $1\frac{1}{4}$ inches by 2 inches   D. $\frac{5}{16}$ inch by 1 inch

8. Express the ratio 3 people out of 100 as a percent.   8. _____
   A. 300%   B. 0.03%   C. 3%   D. 30%

9. Write a percent to represent the shaded area.   9. _____
   A. 9%   B. 16%
   C. 38%   D. 31%

Chapter 11 Test, Form 1A (continued)

10. Express the fraction $\frac{7}{16}$ as a percent.
    A. 0.4375%   **B.** 437.5%   **C.** 4.375%   **D.** 43.75%

    10. _____

11. Express 12% as a fraction in simplest form.
    A. $\frac{12}{1}$ **B.** $\frac{12}{100}$ **C.** $\frac{3}{25}$ **D.** $\frac{6}{50}$

    11. _____

12. Express $6\frac{1}{4}$% as a fraction in simplest form.
    A. $\frac{1}{16}$ **B.** $\frac{25}{400}$ **C.** $\frac{1}{4}$ **D.** $\frac{5}{80}$

    12. _____

13. Express 0.047 as a percent.
    A. 47%   **B.** 4.7%   **C.** 0.47%   **D.** 0.047%

    13. _____

14. Express 3% as a decimal.
    A. 0.03   **B.** 3.0   **C.** 0.3   **D.** 30.0

    14. _____

15. Express 0.89% as a decimal.
    A. 0.0089   **B.** 89.0   **C.** 8.9   **D.** 0.089

    15. _____

16. Express 560% as a decimal.
    A. 56.0   **B.** 0.56   **C.** 5.6   **D.** 560.0

    16. _____

17. Express $1\frac{3}{5}$ as a percent.
    A. 13.5%   **B.** 135%   **C.** 160%   **D.** 16%

    17. _____

18. Replace ● with the correct symbol in $17 \times \frac{5}{6}$ ● $17 \times 83\frac{1}{3}$% to make a true statement.
    A. <   **B.** >   **C.** =   **D.** cannot be determined

    18. _____

19. The Fabulous Flower Shop sells roses at $25.99 for a dozen. Alice's Flower Shop sells roses at $12.99 for a half dozen. At Danitra's, roses sell for $2.25 each, and at Just Flowers, they sell for $8.65 for 4 roses. Which shop has the best buy for roses?
    A. Fab. Flowers   **B.** Alice's
    C. Danitra's   **D.** Just Flowers

    19. _____

20. Alexander folds a piece of paper in half and tears the paper along the fold. He then takes one of the pieces, folds it in half and tears it along the fold. How many pieces of paper will Alexander have if he folds and tears 13 times?
    A. 20   **B.** 13   **C.** 14   **D.** 26

    20. _____

BONUS A building actually stands 336 feet high. A scale model of the building stands 4 feet high. What is the scale factor of the model?
    A. 1 inch:84 feet   **B.** 1 inch:7 feet
    C. 1 inch:28 feet   **D.** 84 feet:1 inch

    _____

Form 1B

Chapter 11 Test

1. Express the ratio 3 feet to 21 inches as a fraction in simplest form.   1. _____
   A. $\frac{12}{7}$ B. $\frac{1}{7}$ C. $\frac{36}{21}$ D. $\frac{5}{7}$

2. Express the rate of $1.50 for 25 pencils as a unit rate.   2. _____
   A. 0.06¢ per pencil   B. 60¢ per pencil
   C. 6¢ per pencil   D. 25¢ per pencil

3. Solve the proportion $\frac{51}{y} = \frac{27}{45}$.   3. _____
   A. 30.6   B. 24   C. 85   D. 0.012

For Exercises 4 and 5, find x in each pair of similar polygons.

4. A. 2   B. 2.5   4. _____
   C. 10   D. 1.6

5. A. 3   B. 6.75   5. _____
   C. 7.25   D. 6

6. On a map, the scale is 1 inch:125 miles. What is the actual   6. _____
   distance if the map distance is $2\frac{3}{4}$ inches?
   A. $343\frac{3}{4}$ miles   B. $281\frac{1}{4}$ miles   C. 257 miles   D. 325 miles

7. On a scale drawing, the scale is $\frac{1}{4}$ inch:1 foot. What are the   7. _____
   dimensions in the scale drawing for a room that is 27 feet
   by 20 feet?
   A. $\frac{9}{16}$ inch by $\frac{5}{12}$ inch   B. $13\frac{1}{2}$ inches by 10 inches
   C. $2\frac{1}{4}$ inches by $1\frac{2}{3}$ inches   D. $6\frac{3}{4}$ inches by 5 inches

8. Express the ratio $10 per $100 as a percent.   8. _____
   A. 100%   B. 1%   C. 10%   D. 0.10%

9. Write a percent to represent the shaded area.   9. _____
   A. 12   B. 24
   C. 9   D. 22

Chapter 11 Test, Form 1B (continued)

10. Express the fraction $\frac{5}{8}$ as a percent. **10.** _____
  A. 62.5%   **B.** 0.625%   **C.** 625%   **D.** 6.25%

11. Express 8% as a fraction in simplest form. **11.** _____
  A. $\frac{2}{25}$ **B.** $\frac{8}{100}$ **C.** $\frac{4}{50}$ **D.** $\frac{80}{100}$

12. Express $91\frac{2}{3}$% as a fraction in simplest form. **12.** _____
  A. $\frac{55}{60}$ **B.** $\frac{275}{300}$ **C.** $\frac{11}{4}$ **D.** $\frac{11}{12}$

13. Express 0.055 as a percent. **13.** _____
  A. 0.055%   **B.** 5.5%   **C.** 55%   **D.** 0.55%

14. Express $25\frac{1}{4}$% as a decimal. **14.** _____
  A. 0.2525   **B.** 25.25   **C.** 25.14   **D.** 0.2514

15. Express 0.02% as a decimal. **15.** _____
  A. 2.0   **B.** 0.02   **C.** 0.0002   **D.** 0.002

16. Express 155% as a decimal. **16.** _____
  A. 15.5   **B.** 1.55   **C.** 155.0   **D.** 0.155

17. Express 0.0075 as a percent. **17.** _____
  A. 75%   **B.** 0.75%   **C.** 7.5%   **D.** 0.000075%

18. Replace ● with the correct symbol in $5\frac{3}{4}$ ● 575% to make a true **18.** _____
statement.
  A. <   **B.** >   **C.** =   **D.** cannot be
                                              determined

19. Jamaal wants to make a slide from a picture he has in his photo **19.** _____
album. The picture has a length of 10 inches and a width of
8 inches. If the width of the slide is 1 inch, what will the length
of the slide be?
  A. 1.25 inches **B.** 0.08 inch   **C.** 0.1 inch   **D.** 0.8 inch

20. Eight baseball teams are participating in a double-elimination **20.** _____
contest; that is, each team must lose two games to be out of the
contest. What is the maximum number of games that can be
played in the contest?
  A. 7   **B.** 11   **C.** 15   **D.** 16

BONUS If a person blinks approximately once every 3 seconds, how _____
many times will a person blink in one year? (It is not a leap year.)
  A. 10,512,000   **B.** 175,200
  C. 94,608,000   **D.** 1,576,800

Form 2A

1. Express the ratio 5 hours to 45 minutes as a fraction in simplest form.

2. Express the rate 48 miles in 5 hours as a unit rate.

3. Solve the proportion $\frac{7}{m} = \frac{4}{5}$.

For Exercises 4 and 5, find x in each pair of similar polygons.

4. 7 in. ⟋⟍ 4 in. ⟍⟋ 3 in. x in.

5. 7 cm ▭ x cm ▯ 23 cm 5 cm

6. On a scale drawing, the scale is 1 inch:5 feet. Find the dimensions of a 12 foot by 24 foot room on the scale drawing.

Express each ratio as a percent.

7. 13 out of 100

8. $27.50 per $100

Express each number as a percent.

9. $\frac{6}{16}$

10. 0.085

11. $4\frac{2}{3}$

Express each percent as a fraction in simplest form.

12. 4%

13. $11\frac{1}{9}\%$

Express each percent as a decimal.

14. 7.3%

15. 278%

16. 0.0049%

Replace each ● with <, >, or =.

17. 0.0521 ● 52.1%

18. 1.79 ● 179%

19. A mother cat had 3 kittens in one litter. Each of these kittens grew up and had two litters of 3 kittens each. Use a diagram to find how many "grand kittens" the mother cat has.

20. A family of four went out to eat at a restaurant. Their total bill was $46.69 plus 15% of the bill as a tip. How much did the family spend at the restaurant?

BONUS Write $(5.4 \times 10^{-12})\%$ as a decimal.

1. _____
2. _____
3. _____
4. _____
5. _____
6. _____
7. _____
8. _____
9. _____
10. _____
11. _____
12. _____
13. _____
14. _____
15. _____
16. _____
17. _____
18. _____
19. _____
20. _____
_____

Chapter 11 Test

Form 2B _____

1. Express the ratio 2 pounds to 8 ounces as a fraction in simplest form.

2. Express the rate $1.59 for 3 pounds as a unit rate.

3. Solve the proportion $\frac{x}{6} = \frac{3}{8}$.

For Exercises 4 and 5, find x in each pair of similar polygons.

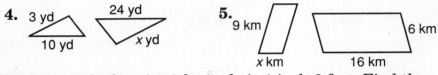

4. 3 yd 10 yd 24 yd x yd

5. 9 km x km 16 km 6 km

6. On a scale drawing, the scale is 1 inch:6 feet. Find the dimensions of an 8 foot by 9 foot room on the scale drawing.

Express each ratio as a percent.

7. 12 out of 100

8. $19.40 per $100

Express each number as a percent.

9. $\frac{15}{24}$

10. 0.045

11. $2\frac{1}{3}$

Express each percent as a fraction in simplest form.

12. 5%

13. $44\frac{4}{9}\%$

Express each percent as a decimal.

14. 8.5%

15. 577%

16. 0.0036%

Replace each ● with <, >, or =.

17. 0.2 ● 10%

18. 4370% ● 437

19. A Central Transit bus is now carrying 53 people, but it can carry a maximum of 70 people. If the bus lets 5 people on and 2 people off at each stop, use a diagram to find how many stops it will take to fill the bus.

20. The results of a survey conducted by the student council of Mt. Ashwood Middle School showed that 9 out of 24 students were planning to attend the spring dance. If there are 1,656 students at Mt. Ashwood, how many students are planning to attend the spring dance?

BONUS A number divided by sixteen is the same as four divided by the number. What is the number?

1. _____

2. _____

3. _____

4. _____

5. _____

6. _____

7. _____

8. _____

9. _____

10. _____

11. _____

12. _____

13. _____

14. _____

15. _____

16. _____

17. _____

18. _____

19. _____

20. _____

_____

Glencoe Division, Macmillan/McGraw-Hill

Use with Lessons 11-1 through 11-5 ━━━━━━━━

Express each ratio as a fraction in simplest form.

1. 54:9   **2.** 21 to 91

Express each rate as a unit rate.

3. $1.16 for 4 pounds   **4.** 320 meters in 20 seconds

Solve each proportion.

5. $\frac{25}{n} = \frac{40}{8}$ **6.** $\frac{z}{48} = \frac{15}{75}$

Find x in each pair of similar polygons.

7. 16 in.   5 in.   **8.**   10 mm   21 mm
4 in.   x in.   12 mm   x mm

On a map, the scale is $\frac{1}{2}$ inch:25 miles. For each map distance, find the actual distance.

9. 3 inches   **10.** $10\frac{1}{2}$ inches

1. _____
2. _____
3. _____
4. _____
5. _____
6. _____
7. _____
8. _____
9. _____
10. _____

Use with Lessons 11-6 through 11-10 ━━━━━━━━

Express each ratio as a percent.

1. 24 hits out of 100   **2.** 7.9:100

3. Express the fraction $\frac{7}{12}$ as a percent.

4. Express $15\frac{1}{2}\%$ as a fraction in simplest form.

5. Express 0.532 as a percent.

6. Express $13\frac{1}{2}$ as a percent.

7. Express 0.7% as a decimal.

8. Express 2.4 as a percent.

9. Replace ● with $<$, $>$, or $=$ in the statement
$12\frac{1}{5}$ ● 1,220%.

10. Olivia mails a poem to three of her friends. Each of her three friends mails the poem to three of their friends, and so on. How many people have the poem after the fifth mailing?

1. _____
2. _____
3. _____
4. _____
5. _____
6. _____
7. _____
8. _____
9. _____
10. _____

97

Cumulative Review Chapters 1-11

1. Evaluate $(75 + 85) \div 4 + 5 \cdot 22$. (Lesson 1-7)

2. Find the mean for the set of data 13, 14, 12, 15, 11, 16 21, 18. (Lesson 3-3)

3. Write $\frac{65}{78}$ in simplest form. (Lesson 4-6)

For Exercises 4 and 5, solve each equation and write the solution in simplest form. (Lessons 5-3, 5-5)

4. $\frac{1}{6} + \frac{5}{9} = b$

5. $m = \frac{14}{15} \times \frac{5}{7}$

6. Find the area of a parallelogram with $b = 9.2$ feet and $h = 7.3$ feet. (Lesson 6-7)

Solve each equation. (Lesson 7-9)

7. $\frac{u}{-12} = -18$

8. $-24 = 6w$

Classify each triangle by its sides and by its angles. (Lesson 8-3)

9.

10.

11. *True* or *false*: A pentagon can be used by itself to make a tessellation. (Lesson 8-6)

12. Use the Pythagorean Theorem to find the length of the hypotenuse of a right triangle if the legs measure 6 centimeters and 5 centimeters. (Lesson 9-4)

13. Find the area of a triangle with a base of 21 feet and a height of 16 feet. (Lesson 9-7)

14. Find the area of a trapezoid with bases of 21 feet and 15 feet and a height of 16 feet. (Lesson 9-7)

Find the surface area of each solid. (Lessons 10-3, 10-4)

15. a rectangular prism with a height of 8.4 millimeters, length 8.8 millimeters, and width 6.2 millimeters

16. a cylinder with a height of 7 feet and a radius of 14 feet

17. a cube with sides of 11.1 yards

18. Express 199.5 miles for 7 gallons as a unit rate. Give your answer to the nearest tenth. (Lesson 11-2)

19. Solve the proportion $\frac{5}{8} = \frac{12}{y}$. (Lesson 11-3)

20. Express the fraction $\frac{17}{44}$ as a percent. (Lesson 11-8)

1. _____
2. _____
3. _____
4. _____
5. _____
6. _____
7. _____
8. _____
9. _____
10. _____
11. _____
12. _____
13. _____
14. _____
15. _____
16. _____
17. _____
18. _____
19. _____
20. _____

Cumulative Test Chapters 1-11

1. Evaluate $21 \times 4 - 55 \div 11$.   1. _____
    A. 2.64   **B.** 79   **C.** 20   **D.** 0

2. Find the mean for the set of data, 4, 9, 1, 6, 2, 2, 7, 3.   2. _____
    A. 4   **B.** 2   **C.** 4.25   **D.** 3.5

3. Write $\frac{114}{216}$ in simplest form.   3. _____
    A. $\frac{1}{6}$ **B.** $\frac{4}{9}$ **C.** $\frac{7}{8}$ **D.** $\frac{19}{36}$

4. Solve the equation $\frac{3}{8} + \frac{7}{12} = s$ and write the answer in 4. _____
    simplest form.
    A. $\frac{10}{20}$ **B.** $\frac{1}{2}$ **C.** $\frac{23}{24}$ **D.** $\frac{7}{12}$

5. Find the area of a parallelogram with a base of 4.2 centimeters   5. _____
    and a height of 9.4 centimeters.
    A. 39.48 cm^2 **B.** 19.74 cm^2 **C.** 13.6 cm^2 **D.** 27.2 cm^2

6. Solve $\frac{n}{3.9} = -11.7$ 6. _____
    A. -3   **B.** 7.8   **C.** -45.63   **D.** 15.6

7. Solve $-92 = -4d$ 7. _____
    A. 23   **B.** 96   **C.** 368   **D.** 88

8. Classify the triangle at the right by its   8. _____
    sides and by its angles.
    A. scalene, right   **B.** scalene, obtuse
    C. scalene, acute   **D.** isosceles, acute

9. Which regular polygon can be used by itself to make a tessellation?   9. _____
    A. hexagon   **B.** pentagon   **C.** octagon   **D.** nonagon

10. Find the length of the leg of a right triangle if its hypotenuse   10. _____
    measures 13 feet and its other leg measures 12 feet.
    A. 17.69 feet   **B.** 1 foot   **C.** 5 feet   **D.** 25 feet

11. Find the area of a triangle with a base of 15.2 m and a height   11. _____
    of 11.4 m.
    A. 173.28 m^2 **B.** 3.8 m^2 **C.** 86.64 m^2 **D.** 26.6 m^2

12. Find the surface area of a prism with length of 24 inches, a   12. _____
    height of 22 inches and a width of 6 inches.
    A. 3,168 in^2 **B.** 104 in^2 **C.** 52 in^2 **D.** 1,608 in^2

13. Find the surface area of a cylinder with height 2.5 mm and   13. _____
    radius 1.6 mm.
    A. 8π mm^2 **B.** 17.62π mm^2
    C. 16π mm^2 **D.** 13.12π mm^2

14. Express $11.99 for twelve boxes as a unit rate.   14. _____
    A. 99¢ per box   **B.** $1.00 per box
    C. $1.99 per box   **D.** 0.99¢ per box

15. Express $\frac{7}{21}$ as a percent.   15. _____
    A. $33\frac{1}{3}\%$ **B.** $\frac{1}{3}\%$ **C.** 7.21%   **D.** 13%

Glencoe Division, Macmillan/McGraw-Hill

Form 1A _____

1. Use a proportion to find $70\frac{1}{2}\%$ of 59. Round your answer to the nearest tenth.
   A. 44.3   **B.** 41.6   **C.** 44.2   **D.** 4.4

   1. _____

2. Use a proportion to find what number is 34% of 34. Round your answer to the nearest tenth.
   A. 100   **B.** 1,156   **C.** 11.6   **D.** 1

   2. _____

3. Estimate 49% of $15\frac{1}{8}$.
   A. 2   **B.** 7.5   **C.** 1   **D.** 4.5

   3. _____

4. Estimate 0.75% of 387.
   A. 300   **B.** 30   **C.** 0.3   **D.** 3

   4. _____

5. Write a proportion and solve to find what number is 48% of 55.
   A. 24.0   **B.** 26.4   **C.** 87.3   **D.** 114.6

   5. _____

6. Write a proportion and solve to find what percent of 184 is 23.
   A. 0.125%   **B.** 8.0%   **C.** 12.5%   **D.** 80%

   6. _____

7. Write an equation and find what number is 74% of 58.
   A. 42.92   **B.** 69.2   **C.** 1.4   **D.** 77.3

   7. _____

8. Write an equation and find what percent of 73 is 99. Round your answer to the nearest whole percent.
   A. 72.27%   **B.** 73%   **C.** 1.36%   **D.** 136%

   8. _____

Use the chart below for Exercises 9-10. The chart displays the results of a survey on the favorite color of all seventh graders at Jones Middle School.

9. Find the ratio that compares the number of students whose favorite color is black with the total number of students. Round your answer to the nearest hundredth.
   A. 0.09   **B.** 0.13   **C.** 0.37   **D.** 0.32

   9. _____

7th Grade Favorite Colors	
Color	**Students**
red	132
blue	114
black	46
green	32
other	32

10. Find the angle measure, to the nearest degree, that would be used to make the section of a circle graph displaying the percent of students whose favorite color is blue.
    A. 133°   **B.** 115°   **C.** 47°   **D.** 32°

    10. _____

Chapter 12 Test, Form 1A (continued)

11. Find the percent of change if the old price is $34.50 and the new price is $24. Round your answer to the nearest whole percent.
    A. 30%　　　B. 11%　　　C. 70%　　　D. 10%

    11. _____

12. Find the percent of change from 4 to 9.
    A. 125%　　　B. 44%　　　C. 56%　　　D. 80%

    12. _____

13. Find the sales tax to the nearest cent on a $25 pair of shoes with 5.75% tax.
    A. $1.44　　　B. $1.43　　　C. $5.75　　　D. $1.77

    13. _____

14. Find the rate of discount if the regular price is $26 and the sale price is $20.80.
    A. 80%　　　B. 2%　　　C. 20%　　　D. 8%

    14. _____

15. Find the interest for a principal of $500, an interest rate of 8%, and a time period of 4 years.
    A. $250　　　B. $1,600　　　C. $660　　　D. $160

    15. _____

16. Find the interest to the nearest cent for a principal of $4,329, an interest rate of 9.25%, and a time period of 18 months.
    A. $4,929.94　　B. $7,207.79　　C. $4,356.25　　D. $600.65

    16. _____

17. Find the interest to the nearest cent on a credit card with a principal of $205, an interest rate of 21%, and a time period of 6 months.
    A. $55.35　　　B. $25.83　　　C. $21.53　　　D. $27.00

    17. _____

18. Angie wants to put a winter coat in layaway at a store. To do so, she must pay the store 20% of the cost of the coat so they will hold it. If the coat costs $48.99, about how much of a deposit does Angie need to pay the store?
    A. $2.50　　　B. $10　　　C. $15　　　D. $5

    18. _____

19. In Juan's math class, there are 16 boys and 9 girls. What percent of Juan's class is girls?
    A. 36%　　　B. 56.25%　　　C. 64%　　　D. 43.75%

    19. _____

20. Albert Groe bought a suit for $295. He used his credit card which charges 19% annual interest from the moment of purchase. If he does not make any payments or any additional charges, how much would he owe at the end of the first month?
    A. $301.73　　B. $56.05　　C. $351.05　　D. $299.67

    20. _____

BONUS In January, Jenny used her credit card to purchase a pair of shoes for $36 and a pair of gloves for $10. She paid half of her bill at the end of the month. In February, she used her same credit card to buy a pair of pants for $22. If her credit card company charges 18.25% annual interest from the moment of purchase, what will Jenny's bill be at the end of February?
    A. $46.04　　　B. $70.07　　　C. $46.36　　　D. $45.69

    _____

Form 1B

Chapter 12 Test

1. Use a proportion to find $17\frac{1}{4}$% of 84. Round your answer to the nearest tenth.
   A. 1449 **B.** 14.5 **C.** 20.5 **D.** 14.4

   1. _____

2. Use a proportion to find what number is 2% of 800.
   A. 4 **B.** 1,600 **C.** 400 **D.** 16

   2. _____

3. Estimate 35% of $293\frac{1}{2}$.
   A. 125 **B.** 75 **C.** 100 **D.** 150

   3. _____

4. Estimate 396% of 24.
   A. 75 **B.** 6 **C.** 100 **D.** 15

   4. _____

5. Write a proportion and solve to find what number is 64% of 25.
   A. 15 **B.** 2.6 **C.** 39.1 **D.** 16

   5. _____

6. Write a proportion and solve to find 89% of what number is 14. Round your answer to the nearest tenth.
   A. 14.0 **B.** 15.7 **C.** 6.4 **D.** 12.5

   6. _____

7. Write an equation and find what number is 97% of 48.
   A. 49.48 **B.** 46.56 **C.** 45.98 **D.** 23.28

   7. _____

8. Write an equation and find what percent of 55 is 10. Round your answer to the nearest whole percent.
   A. 6% **B.** 18% **C.** 2% **D.** 550%

   8. _____

Use the chart below for Exercises 9-10. The chart displays the results of a survey on the average amount of time seventh graders at Smith Middle School spend watching television each day.

9. Find the ratio that compares the number of students who watch 3-4 hours of television with the total number of students. Round your answer to the nearest hundredth.
   A. 0.54 **B.** 0.27 **C.** 0.38 **D.** 0.13

   9. _____

Time Watching TV	
Time	**Students**
0-1 hours	70
1-2 hours	112
2-3 hours	156
3-4 hours	54
4 or more hours	23

10. Find the angle measure, to the nearest degree, that would be used to make the section of a circle graph displaying the percent of students who watch 0-1 hours of television each night.
    A. 56° **B.** 17° **C.** 70° **D.** 61°

    10. _____

Chapter 12 Test, Form 1B (continued)

11. Find the percent of change if the old price is $47 and the new price is $21. Round your answer to the nearest whole percent.
   A. 45%   **B.** 55%   **C.** 26%   **D.** 50%

11. _____

12. Find the percent of change from 11 to 29. Round your answer to the nearest whole percent.
   A. 18%   **B.** 38%   **C.** 164%   **D.** 3%

12. _____

13. Find the discount on a $70 jacket that is 25% off.
   A. $52.50   **B.** $17.50   **C.** $55   **D.** $2.80

13. _____

14. Find the rate of discount to the nearest percent if the regular price is $38 and the sale price is $19.60.
   A. 48%   **B.** 3%   **C.** 7%   **D.** 70%

14. _____

15. Find the interest for a principal of $950, an interest rate of 6.75%, and a time period of 2 years.
   A. $10.69   **B.** $281.48   **C.** $128.25   **D.** $70.37

15. _____

16. Find the interest to the nearest cent for a principal of $250, an interest rate of 11.25%, and a time period of 4 months.
   A. $112.50   **B.** $7.40   **C.** $88.89   **D.** $9.38

16. _____

17. Find the interest to the nearest cent on a credit card with a principal of $73.99, an interest rate of 19.5%, and a time period of 21 months.
   A. $25.25   **B.** $79.68   **C.** $302.99   **D.** $68.71

17. _____

18. A telemarketing company makes an average of 195 calls in one night. Each operator working for the company makes about 20% of the total number of calls. About how many calls will an operator make in one night?
   A. 5   **B.** 40   **C.** 10   **D.** 20

18. _____

19. Anita sent out invitations to a party and received an RSVP from every invitation. Thirteen of the RSVPs came back with a yes response and six RSVPs came back with a no response. What percent of the people Anita invited to her party are not coming? Round your answer to the nearest percent.
   A. 68%   **B.** 46%   **C.** 32%   **D.** 19%

19. _____

20. Ramone went out with his friends to a restaurant and the bill for his food was $7.95 before tax and tip were added. If 5.5% tax is added and then 15% of that cost is calculated for a tip, how much will Ramone spend at the restaurant?
   A. $14.17   **B.** $9.65   **C.** $9.58   **D.** $9.64

20. _____

BONUS There are 20 students running for student council at Pine Bluff High School. If the school will elect a president, vice president, treasurer, and secretary, what percent of the students running will win in the election?
   A. 5%   **B.** 4%   **C.** 25%   **D.** 20%

_____

103

Form 2A _____ *Chapter 12 Test*

1. Use a proportion to find $55\frac{1}{2}\%$ of 66. Round your answer to the nearest tenth.

2. Use a proportion to find what number is 78% of 78. Round your answer to the nearest tenth.

3. Estimate 0.25% of 814.

4. Write a proportion and solve to find what number is 97% of 16. Round your answer to the nearest tenth.

5. Write an equation and find 19% of what number is 31. Round your answer to the nearest tenth.

6. Write an equation and find what percent of 49 is 40. Round your answer to the nearest whole percent.

7. The graph at the right displays the results of a survey of 163 seventh-grade pet owners at JFK Middle School. Use the graph to find which pet can be described by $\frac{20}{163}$.

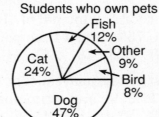

Students who own pets

8. Find the percent of change if the old price is $65.99 and the new price is $72.99. Round your answer to the nearest whole percent.

9. Find the percent of change from 7 to 3. Round your answer to the nearest whole percent.

10. Find the sale price of a $57 pair of shoes on sale for 20% off.

11. Find the interest for a principal of $2,500, an interest rate of 8.75%, and a time period of 24 months.

12. Find the interest on a credit card with a principal of $855, an interest rate of 19%, and a time period of 4 months.

13. DaShawna baby-sits for $3 an hour. She wants to buy a shirt that is selling for $15.95 and a pair of pants that are selling for $21.99. About how many hours will she need to baby-sit before she will have enough money to buy both the shirt and pants?

14. At Oakwood Middle School, Ms. Addams and Mr. Kleckner are the seventh-grade math teachers. Ms. Addams teaches 84 students, and Mr. Kleckner teaches 53 students. What percent of the students does Ms. Addams teach? Round your answer to the nearest whole percent.

15. Find the total purchase price to the nearest cent if a $95 radio is on sale for 25% off and the sales tax is 5.75%.

BONUS To the nearest whole percent, 44% of the seventh-graders at King Middle School are girls. There are 428 seventh-graders. What are all the possibilities for the number of girls in the seventh grade?

1. _____

2. _____

3. _____

4. _____

5. _____

6. _____

7. _____

8. _____

9. _____

10. _____

11. _____

12. _____

13. _____

14. _____

15. _____

_____

Form 2B _____

1. Use a proportion to find $19\frac{1}{4}\%$ of 45. Round your answer to the nearest tenth.

2. Use a proportion to find what number is 7% of 588. Round your answer to the nearest tenth.

3. Estimate 309% of 26.

4. Write a proportion and solve to find 63% of what number is 9. Round your answer to the nearest tenth.

5. Write an equation and find what number is 19% of 46. Round your answer to the nearest tenth.

6. Write an equation and find what percent of 32 is 69. Round your answer to the nearest whole percent.

7. The circle graph at the right displays the percent of 142 seventh-graders at Lincoln Middle School with each hair color. Use the graph to find which hair color is represented by the ratio $\frac{55}{142}$.

Hair Color
Blonde 10%
Black 39%
Red 5%
Brown 43%
Other 3%

8. Find the percent of change if the old price is $36 and the new price is $26. Round your answer to the nearest whole percent.

9. Find the percent of change from 44 to 49. Round your answer to the nearest whole percent.

10. Find the discount on a $79 jacket that is 30% off.

11. Find the total purchase price to the nearest cent of a $5.99 toy with 6.5% tax.

12. Find the interest to the nearest cent for a principal of $1,900, an interest rate of 13.25%, and a time of 32 months.

13. Eric mows lawns at a rate of $5/lawn. He wants to start saving to buy a bike that costs $95 and a bike helmet that costs $24.50. About how many lawns will he need to mow before he can buy both the bike and the helmet?

14. There are 24 boy scouts and 31 girls scouts at East Middle School. To the nearest whole percent, what percent of the scouts are boys?

15. Fred went shopping for school clothes. He used the same credit card to buy 2 pairs of pants for $30.98 and 3 shirts for $41.74. His credit card company charges 19.5% annual interest from the moment of purchase. If he does not make any additional charges or payments, how much would he owe at the end of the first month?

BONUS Fifty percent of what amount would be the same as twenty-five percent of thirty-five dollars?

1. _____
2. _____
3. _____
4. _____
5. _____
6. _____
7. _____
8. _____
9. _____
10. _____
11. _____
12. _____
13. _____
14. _____
15. _____
_____

Use with Lessons 12-1 through 12-5 _____ **Chapter 12, Quiz A**

1. Use a proportion to find 65% of 58.
2. Use a proportion to find what number is 5% of 85.
3. Estimate 156% of 77.
4. Estimate 0.55% of 781.
5. Write a proportion and solve to find 21% of what number is 84. Round your answer to the nearest tenth.
6. Write a proportion and solve to find what percent of 76 is 289. Round your answer to the nearest whole percent.
7. Write an equation and find 66% of what number is 65. Round your answer to the nearest tenth.
8. Write an equation and find 8% of 55. Round your answer to the nearest tenth.
9. If 69% of the 247 students in the seventh grade ride the bus to school, about how many students do not take the bus to school?
10. There were 102,269 tickets available for a rock concert. If The Ticket Company sold 72.5% of the tickets available, about how many tickets did they sell for the concert?

1. _____
2. _____
3. _____
4. _____
5. _____
6. _____
7. _____
8. _____
9. _____
10. _____

- -

Use with Lessons 12-6 through 12-9 _____ **Chapter 12, Quiz B**

1. If 117 out of 431 students have a dog for a pet, find the ratio that compares the students who have a dog with the total number of students. Round your answer to the nearest hundredth.
2. Use the information in Exercise 1 to find the angle measure, to the nearest degree, that would be used to make a section of a circle graph displaying the percent of students who have a dog for a pet.
3. Find the percent of change if the old price is $72.42 and the new price is $62.18. Round your answer to the nearest whole percent.
4. Find the total purchase price to the nearest cent of an electric garage door opener that normally sells for $159.99 is on sale for 30% off and the sales tax is 6.25%.
5. Lissa Cantiti bought a suit for $159. She used her credit card which charges 21% annual interest from the moment of purchase. If she does not make any payment or additional charges, how much would she owe at the end of the first month?

1. _____
2. _____
3. _____
4. _____
5. _____

Cumulative Review Chapters 1-12

1. Complete 1.27 L = ☐mL. (Lesson 2-9)

2. Write the prime factorization of 180. (Lesson 4-2)

3. Find the perimeter of a rectangle with $l = 3\frac{1}{4}$ feet and $w = 2\frac{2}{3}$ feet. (Lesson 5-6)

4. How many quarts are in $6\frac{1}{4}$ gallons? (Lesson 6-6)

5. Name the integer represented by P. Then find its opposite and absolute value. (Lesson 7-1)

P
-6 -4 -2 0 2 4 6

6. The measure of an angle is 91°. Classify the angle as right, acute, obtuse, or straight. (Lesson 8-1)

7. Determine if the figure at the right is a polygon. If not, explain why. (Lesson 8-2)

8. Find $\sqrt{289}$. (Lesson 9-2)

9. Find the best whole number estimate for $\sqrt{61}$. (Lesson 9-3)

10. Find the area of a circle with diameter 8.5 cm. (Lesson 9-8)

11. Find the surface area of a cylinder whose height is 14.8 inches and whose base has a diameter of 2.5 inches. (Lesson 10-4)

12. Find the volume of a rectangular prism with a length of 4 meters, a width of 6 meters, and a height of 11 meters. (Lesson 10-5)

13. Find the volume of a cylinder whose height is 5.2 millimeters and whose radius is 6.4 millimeters. (Lesson 10-6)

14. Express the ratio 24:33 as a fraction in simplest form. (Lesson 11-1)

15. Solve the proportion $\frac{a}{6} = \frac{25}{30}$. (Lesson 11-3)

16. Amanda wants to make a slide from a picture of her trip to Florida. The photo has a width of 4 inches and a length of 7 inches. If the width of the slide is 1 inch, what will be the length of the slide? (Lesson 11-5)

17. Express 3.45% as a decimal. (Lesson 11-9)

18. Estimate 11% of 58.2. (Lesson 12-3)

19. Find the percent of change if the old price is $52 and the new price is $35. Round to the nearest whole percent. (Lesson 12-7)

20. Find the interest to the nearest cent for a principal of $4,000, an interest rate of 8.25%, and a time of 21 months. (Lesson 12-9)

1. _____
2. _____
3. _____
4. _____
5. _____
6. _____
7. _____
8. _____
9. _____
10. _____
11. _____
12. _____
13. _____
14. _____
15. _____
16. _____
17. _____
18. _____
19. _____
20. _____

Glencoe Division, Macmillan/McGraw-Hill

Cumulative Test Chapters 1-12

1. $31 \text{ g} = \square \text{ kg}$
   A. 310   **B.** 0.31   **C.** 3.1   **D.** 0.031

   1. _____

2. Write the prime factorization of 84.
   A. $2 \cdot 2 \cdot 3 \cdot 7$ **B.** $2 \cdot 3 \cdot 3 \cdot 7$ **C.** $2 \cdot 3 \cdot 7$ **D.** $2 \cdot 3 \cdot 21$

   2. _____

3. Find the mean of 22, 22, 23, 28, and 30.
   A. 22   **B.** 25   **C.** 23   **D.** 125

   3. _____

4. How many pints are in $2\frac{1}{2}$ gallons?
   A. 20 pints   **B.** 40 pints   **C.** 10 pints   **D.** 5 pints

   4. _____

5. Evaluate $a^2 + 2b$ if $a = 5$ and $b = 3$.
   A. 31   **B.** 13   **C.** 8   **D.** 16

   5. _____

6. Which figure is *not* a polygon.
   A.   **B.**   **C.**   **D.**

   6. _____

7. Estimate $\sqrt{174}$.
   A. 13   **B.** 14   **C.** 12   **D.** 16

   7. _____

8. Find the area of a circle with diameter 7.4 cm.
   A. 23.2 cm^2 **B.** 171.9 cm^2 **C.** 43.0 cm^2 **D.** 46.5 cm^2

   8 _____

9. Find the surface area of a cylinder whose height is 9.1 inches and whose base has a diameter of 8 inches.
   A. 859.1 in^2 **B.** 457.2 in^2 **C.** 1828.7 in^2 **D.** 329.1 in^2

   9. _____

10. Find the volume of a cylinder whose height is 8.2 mm and whose radius is 3.9 mm.
    A. 124.7 mm^2 **B.** 823.8 mm^2 **C.** 100.4 mm^2 **D.** 391.6 mm^2

    10. _____

11. Express the ratio 33:54 as a fraction in simplest form.
    A. $\frac{33}{54}$ **B.** $\frac{11}{18}$ **C.** $\frac{3}{5}$ **D.** $\frac{30}{50}$

    11. _____

12. Solve the proportion $\frac{a}{10} = \frac{35}{50}$.
    A. 7.2   **B.** 1   **C.** 7   **D.** 350

    12. _____

13. A room is 24 feet in length. On a scale drawing, 1 inch represents 8 feet. What is the length of the room in the scale drawing?
    A. $\frac{1}{3}$ inch   **B.** 192 inches   **C.** 3 inches   **D.** 2.5 inches

    13. _____

14. Estimate 47% of 1,035.
    A. 100   **B.** 50   **C.** 250   **D.** 500

    14. _____

15. Yoli borrowed $1,200 from the bank with an interest rate of 12.75%. How much interest will she pay after 30 months?
    A. $382.50   **B.** $3,825.00   **C.** $4,590.00   **D.** $61.20

    15. _____

Form 1A

Chapter 13 Test

1. Justine is taking a test with four true/false questions on it. Use a tree diagram to find how many possible ways the four answers could appear on the test.

   A. 4   **B.** 8   **C.** 16   **D.** 32

   1. _____

2. Use multiplication to find the number of outcomes that are possible if you toss a penny, a nickel, and a quarter.

   A. 8   **B.** 3   **C.** 2   **D.** 10

   2. _____

Cory has two tickets to a baseball game. He can take one of his friends with him, but five of his friends would like to go. They are Jane, Meg, Mike, Tony, and Amy. To decide, Cory writes each of his friends' names on a separate piece of paper and selects one. Use this information to answer Exercises 3–5.

3. What is the probability that Cory picks a girl?

   A. $\frac{1}{5}$ **B.** $\frac{2}{5}$ **C.** $\frac{2}{3}$ **D.** $\frac{3}{5}$

   3. _____

4. What is the probability that Cory picks someone whose name does not begin with the letter M?

   A. $\frac{2}{5}$ **B.** $\frac{3}{5}$ **C.** $\frac{1}{2}$ **D.** $\frac{1}{6}$

   4. _____

5. If Cory draws a name 20 times and Amy's name is picked twice, what is the experimental probability that Amy will go to the game?

   A. $\frac{1}{5}$ **B.** $\frac{2}{5}$ **C.** $\frac{1}{10}$ **D.** $\frac{1}{6}$

   5. _____

The spinner at the right has an equal chance of landing on each number. Use the spinner for Exercises 6 and 7.

6. Find P(an odd number, then an even number).

   A. $\frac{7}{7}$ **B.** $\frac{12}{49}$ **C.** $\frac{7}{49}$ **D.** $\frac{2}{49}$

   6. _____

7. Find P(3, then 6).

   A. $\frac{1}{2}$ **B.** $\frac{1}{7}$ **C.** $\frac{2}{49}$ **D.** $\frac{1}{49}$

   7. _____

8. Alex draws a card from a standard deck of 52 cards. Without replacing the first card, he draws a second one. What is P(club, then club)?

   A. $\frac{1}{169}$ **B.** $\frac{1}{17}$ **C.** $\frac{1}{26}$ **D.** $\frac{1}{16}$

   8. _____

9. Benji has 3 pairs of pants to wear to school. What is the probability that he will wear the same pair of pants more than once in a 5-day school week?

   A. $\frac{3}{5}$ **B.** $\frac{2}{5}$ **C.** 1   **D.** $\frac{5}{3}$

   9. _____

Chapter 13 Test Form 1A continued

Of 350,000 registered voters, 800 were surveyed. Their voting preferences are listed in the chart at the right. Use the chart for Exercises 10–12.

Candidate	Votes
Carroll	154
Ledo	268
Sanchez	218
Undecided	160

10. What percent of the registered voters are undecided?
    A. 20% **B.** 80% **C.** 0.04% **D.** 25%

10. _____

11. How many registered voters can be expected to vote for Sanchez?
    A. 1,606 **B.** 174,400 **C.** 218 **D.** 95,375

11. _____

12. If one half of the undecided voters vote for Sanchez and the other half vote for Carroll, who can be expected to win?
    A. Sanchez **B.** Ledo **C.** Carroll **D.** no winner

12 _____

13. Evaluate 6!.
    A. 21 **B.** 120 **C.** 1 **D.** 720

13. _____

14. Evaluate $P(4, 4)$.
    A. 24 **B.** 0 **C.** 2 **D.** 10

14. _____

15. Evaluate $P(8, 3)$.
    A. 6,561 **B.** 512 **C.** 336 **D.** 6,720

15. _____

16. Evaluate $\frac{0!}{5!}$.
    A. $\frac{1}{120}$ **B.** 0 **C.** $\frac{1}{5}$ **D.** undefined

16. _____

17. Evaluate $\frac{9!}{5!}$.
    A. 3,024 **B.** 24 **C.** 6,561 **D.** 59,049

17. _____

18. Evaluate $C(7, 4)$.
    A. 210 **B.** 840 **C.** 35 **D.** 9

18. _____

19. There were 10 different food items in the salad bar. If Phillip made three trips to the salad bar and chose only one different food item each time, in how many ways could he have selected his food?
    A. 1,000 **B.** 604,800 **C.** 30 **D.** 720

19. _____

20. Carol is in the 7th grade at North Middle School and is making out her 8th grade schedule. She can select two of the 9 courses she will take from the following options: French, Spanish, home economics, industrial technology, art and music. What is the probability that Carol will select industrial technology and music?
    A. $\frac{1}{3}$ **B.** $\frac{1}{15}$ **C.** $\frac{2}{9}$ **D.** $\frac{1}{30}$

20. _____

BONUS A deli uses six kinds of meat to make their sandwiches. Their menu lists one fourth of the possible sandwiches that can be made with three kinds of meat and one fifth of the possible sandwiches that can be made with two kinds of meat. How many sandwiches are listed on the menu?
    A. 12 **B.** 15 **C.** 7 **D.** 8

_____

Chapter 13 Test

Form 1B

1. Janet has 4 blouses, 2 pairs of pants, and 3 pairs of socks that can be worn together. Use a tree diagram to find how many outfits she can make.

   A. 9   **B.** 18   **C.** 20   **D.** 24

   1. _____

2. Use multiplication to find the total number of choices you have in buying a car if you can select from 2 models, 3 colors, and 5 option packages.

   A. 10   **B.** 16   **C.** 30   **D.** 25

   2. _____

Tory has two tickets to a football game. She can take one of her friends with her, but five of her friends would like to go. They are Tom, Jill, Joe, Marvin, and Ginger. To decide, Tory writes each of her friends' names on a separate piece of paper and selects one. Use this information to answer Exercises 3–5.

3. What is the probability that Tory picks a boy?

   A. $\frac{3}{5}$ **B.** $\frac{1}{5}$ **C.** $\frac{2}{3}$ **D.** $\frac{2}{5}$

   3. _____

4. What is the probability that Tory picks someone whose name begins with the letters J or M?

   A. $\frac{3}{5}$ **B.** $\frac{2}{5}$ **C.** $\frac{1}{2}$ **D.** $\frac{1}{6}$

   4. _____

5. If Tory draws a name 15 times and Tom's name is picked five times, what is the experimental probability that Tom will go to the game?

   A. $\frac{5}{5}$ **B.** $\frac{1}{5}$ **C.** $\frac{1}{3}$ **D.** $\frac{5}{6}$

   5. _____

The spinner at the right has an equal chance of landing on each number. Use the spinner for Exercises 6 and 7.

6. Find P(odd number, then odd number).

   A. $\frac{4}{7}$ **B.** $\frac{1}{7}$ **C.** $\frac{16}{49}$ **D.** $\frac{8}{49}$

   6. _____

7. Find P(6, then 6).

   A. $\frac{1}{49}$ **B.** $\frac{2}{7}$ **C.** $\frac{4}{49}$ **D.** $\frac{1}{9}$

   7. _____

8. Margaret draws a card from a standard deck of 52 cards. Without replacing the first one, she draws a second one. What is P(3, then 3)?

   A. $\frac{1}{169}$ **B.** $\frac{1}{221}$ **C.** $\frac{3}{676}$ **D.** $\frac{30}{221}$

   8. _____

9. Karen has 4 sweaters and she wears one to school each day. Find the probability that she will wear the same sweater more than once in a 5-day school week.

   A. $\frac{4}{5}$ **B.** 1   **C.** $\frac{5}{4}$ **D.** $\frac{1}{5}$

   9. _____

Chapter 13 Test Form 1B (continued)

Of 350,000 registered voters, 800 were surveyed. Their voting preferences are listed in the chart at the right. Use the chart for Exercises 10–12.

Candidate	Votes
Carroll	172
Ledo	250
Sanchez	198
Undecided	180

10. What percent of the registered voters are undecided?

    A. 0.225% **B.** 1.8% **C.** 18% **D.** 22.5%

10. _____

11. How many of the registered voters can be expected to vote for Ledo?

    A. 109,375 **B.** 252 **C.** 201,600 **D.** 1,389

11. _____

12. If one half of the undecided voters vote for Carroll and the other half do not vote, who can be expected to win?

    A. Sanchez **B.** Ledo **C.** Carroll **D.** no winner

12. _____

13. Evaluate 4!.

    A. 256 **B.** 10 **C.** 4 **D.** 24

13. _____

14. Evaluate $P(8, 5)$.

    A. 6,720 **B.** 32,768 **C.** 1,680 **D.** 336

14. _____

15. Evaluate $\frac{3!}{1!}$.

    A. 3 **B.** 7 **C.** 6 **D.** undefined

15. _____

16. Evaluate $\frac{5!}{5!}$.

    A. 1 **B.** 25 **C.** 0 **D.** 3,125

16. _____

17. Evaluate $C(8, 2)$.

    A. 56 **B.** 10,080 **C.** 28 **D.** 720

17. _____

18. Evaluate $C(3, 0)$.

    A. 3 **B.** 1 **C.** 6 **D.** undefined

18. _____

19. Edward is making out his schedule for 8th grade. He will have 6 classes each day, and there are 9 courses to choose from. In how many ways can he schedule his classes?

    A. 54 **B.** 60,480 **C.** 504 **D.** 84

19. _____

20. Ten students are trying out for a school quartet. In how many ways can the members be selected?

    A. 1,260 **B.** 210 **C.** 40 **D.** 5,040

20. _____

BONUS Joanne is taking a 10-question multiple-choice test. The first five of the questions have 4 choices for answers and the last five have 5 choices for answers. In how many possible ways can the answers be listed for the test? (Hint: Use a tree diagram as a start.)

_____

    A. 3,750 **B.** 1,953,125 **C.** 3,200,000 **D.** 4,149

Chapter 13 Test

Form 2A

1. Use a tree diagram to find the number of ways you can arrange the letters W, X, Y, and Z.

2. Use multiplication to find the number of "faces" you can make with 3 eye colors, 4 hair colors, and 3 types of noses.

A cafeteria vending machine contains apples, chicken sandwiches, potato salad, gelatin, lettuce salad, and pudding. Without looking, you select one of the items. Use this information to answer Exercises 3 and 4.

3. Find P(selecting a type of salad).

4. Find P(not selecting a chicken sandwich).

5. Jeanette has 6 hair ribbons and she wears one every day. What is the probability that she will wear the same ribbon more than once in one week?

Of 250,000 registered voters, 600 were surveyed. Their voting preferences are listed in the chart at the right. Use the chart to answer Exercises 6 and 7.

Candidate	Votes
Owens	144
Warren	98
Russell	252
Undecided	106

6. What percent of registered voters can be expected to vote for Owens?

7. If the undecided vote for Owens, who can be expected to win?

A bag contains red, blue, yellow, green, and orange marbles. There are five marbles of each color in the bag. Use this information to answer Exercises 8 and 9.

8. What is P(blue, then blue) if you do not replace the first marble after you draw it?

9. What is P(red, then orange) if you replace the first marble after you draw it?

10. Evaluate 0!.

11. Evaluate $P(6, 2)$.

12. Evaluate $\frac{7!}{3!}$.

13. Evaluate $C(4, 3)$.

14. Joey can seat three people in the back seat of his car. In how many different ways can three friends sit in the back seat of his car?

15. For English class, Angela must read 5 books from a list of 8. In how many different ways can Angela complete her assignment if the order in which she reads them is not important?

BONUS On a spinner with whole numbers, there is an equal chance of landing on any one of the sections. What is P(you land on an even number) + P(you land on an odd number)?

1. _____
2. _____
3. _____
4. _____
5. _____
6. _____
7. _____
8. _____
9. _____
10. _____
11. _____
12. _____
13. _____
14. _____
15. _____
_____

Form 2B

1. Use a tree diagram to find how many different ways you can arrange the numbers 1, 4, and 5 if no number can be used more than once.

2. Use multiplication to find the number of "faces" you can create with 2 different eye colors, 3 different wigs, 2 different noses, and 1 mouth.

A cafeteria vending machine contains apples, chicken sandwiches, potato salad, gelatin, lettuce salad, and pudding. Without looking, you select one of the items. Use this information to answer Exercises 3 and 4.

3. Find P(selecting gelatin or pudding).

4. Find P(you select a fruit).

5. Antonio has 3 favorite pencils. If he uses one of them to do his homework every night, what is the probability that he will use the same pencil more than once in a 5-day school week?

Of 250,000 registered voters, 600 were surveyed. Their voting preferences are listed in the chart at the right. Use the chart to answer Exercises 6 and 7.

Candidate	Votes
Owens	111
Warren	168
Russell	217
Undecided	104

6. What percent of registered voters can be expected to vote for Warren?

7. If half of the undecided vote for Owens and the other half vote for Warren, who will be expected to win the election?

A bag contains red, blue, yellow, green, and orange marbles. There are five marbles of each color in the bag. Use this information to answer Exercises 8 and 9.

8. What is P(green, then red) if you do not replace the first marble after you draw it?

9. What is P(yellow, yellow) if you replace the first marble after you pick it?

10. Evaluate 5!.

11. Evaluate $P(9, 2)$.

12. Evaluate $\frac{5!}{4!}$

13. Evaluate $C(5, 3)$.

14. Determine the number of ways you can arrange 3 women, 3 men, and 2 children in a line.

15. Orville's assignment for art class is to complete 4 projects from a list of 6. In how many ways can Orville do this if the order in which he does them is not important?

BONUS How many monograms each having 3-letter initials are possible?

1. _____
2. _____
3. _____
4. _____
5. _____
6. _____
7. _____
8. _____
9. _____
10. _____
11. _____
12. _____
13. _____
14. _____
15. _____

_____

Chapter 13 Quiz A (Lessons 13-1 through 13-4)

1. Use a tree diagram to find how many ways you can arrange four colors, yellow, red, blue, and black if no color can be used more than once.

   1. _____

2. Cathy is dressing a store mannequin and can choose from an assortment of clothes consisting of 3 summer dresses, 2 winter dresses, 5 hats, and 2 pairs of shoes. Use multilication to find how many different ways Cathy can dress the mannequin with a dress, a hat, and a pair of shoes.

   2. _____

Out of 25 rolls of a die, Cecil rolls a 5 four times. Use this information to answer Exercises 3 and 4.

3. What is the experimental probability of rolling a 5?

   3. _____

4. What is the theoretical probability of rolling a 5?

   4. _____

5. Ashley has 5 different colors of fingernail polish, clear, pink, red, silver, and beige. If she selects a polish at random, what is the probability it will be clear or silver?

   5. _____

Chapter 13 Quiz B (Lessons 13-5 through 13-8)

Two hundred people chosen at random in a town of 10,500 people were asked what radio station they listen to in the morning. Forty-four of them said they listen to WXMT. Use this information to answer Exercises 1 and 2.

1. What percent of people in the town listen to WXMT in the morning?

   1. _____

2. How many people in the town can be expected to listen to WXMT in the morning?

   2. _____

Cards with the words *win, lose,* and *try again* are placed in a bag. There are 2 win cards, 10 lose cards, and 4 try again cards. Use this information to answer Exercises 3 and 4.

   3. _____

   4. _____

3. Find P(drawing a win card).

   5. _____

4. Find P(drawing a lose card).

   6. _____

5. Evaluate 2!.   6.   Evaluate $P(4, 2)$.

   7. _____

7. Evaluate $\frac{9!}{3!}$.   8.   Evaluate $C(8, 5)$.

   8. _____

9. Determine the number of ways you can arrange 4 women and 3 men in a line.

   9. _____

10. Determine the number of ways you can seat 4 women and 3 men in four chairs.

    10. _____

Cumulative Review Chapters 1-13

1. Evaluate $a^2 + 2b$ if $a = 5$ and $b = 9$. (Lesson 1–9)

2. Find the mode(s) of 6, 2, 5, 5, 7, 1. (Lesson 3-5)

3. Subtract $\frac{5}{6} - \frac{1}{8}$. (Lesson 5-3)

4. Solve $\frac{m}{19} = 3$. (Lesson 6-1)

5. Multiply $-14 \times (-9)$. (Lesson 7-7)

6. Give all names that describe the quadrilateral at the right. Underline the best choice. (Lesson 8-3)

7. Find the length of a leg of a right triangle whose hypotenuse measures 12 units and whose other leg measures 9 units. (Lesson 9-5)

8. Find the square of 16. (Lesson 9-2)

9. Find the area of a triangle with base 7.2 inches and height 8.5 inches. (Lesson 9-7)

10. Find the volume of a cylinder: radius 7 cm and height 4.5 cm. (Lesson 10-6)

11. Find the surface area of a rectangular prism: length 4 yards, width 3.2 yards, and height 3.3 yards. (Lesson 10-3)

12. Express the rate of *288 miles for 12 gallons* as a unit rate. (Lesson 11-2)

13. Write 77% as a decimal. (Lesson 11-9)

14. Jeanine answered 43 out of 50 questions on her test correctly. Find the percent she answered correctly. (Lesson 12-4)

15. What number of degrees in a circle graph represents the ratio $\frac{51}{268}$? (Lesson 12-6)

16. Find the purchase price of a $10.99 T-shirt on sale for 15% off with 6.5% sales tax. (Lesson 12-8)

17. Estimate 32% of 16. (Lesson 12-3)   18. Evaluate $C(9, 3)$. (Lesson 13-8)

19. If 26 of 100 students at Hammond School selected at random said they like math the most, how many of the 1,550 students at Hammond would you expect to like math the most? (Lesson 13-5)

20. The spinner at the right has an equal chance of landing on each number. Find P(odd number, then odd number). (Lesson 13-6)

1. _____

2. _____

3. _____

4. _____

5. _____

6. _____

7. _____

8. _____

9. _____

10. _____

11. _____

12. _____

13. _____

14. _____

15. _____

16. _____

17. _____

18. _____

19. _____

20. _____

Cumulative Test Chapters 1-13

1. Find the range of 42, 26, 18, 27, 60, 41, and 32.
   A. 60   **B.** 41   **C.** 42   **D.** 78   1. _____

2. Find the prime factorization of 96.
   A. $2 \cdot 3$ **B.** $2^2 \cdot 3 \cdot 8$ **C.** $2^5 \cdot 3$ **D.** $2 \cdot 48$ 2. _____

3. Subtract $\frac{4}{5} - \frac{4}{9}$.
   A. $\frac{16}{45}$ **B.** 0   **C.** 1   **D.** $\frac{36}{45}$ 3. _____

4. Solve $\frac{p}{20} = 4$.
   A. 80   **B.** 5   **C.** 0.2   **D.** 24   4. _____

5. Multiply $-18 \times (-6)$.
   A. -108 **B.** 3   **C.** 108   **D.** -3 5. _____

6. Find the length of the hypotenuse of a right triangle whose long leg measures 8 units and whose short leg measures 2 units.
   A. 7.7 units   **B.** 10 units   **C.** 16 units   **D.** 8.2 units   6. _____

7. Find the square of 25.
   A. 5   **B.** 625   **C.** 50   **D.** 125   7. _____

8. Find the area of a triangle whose base is 7.4 m and whose height is 4.6 m.
   A. 17.02 m²   **B.** 6 m²   **C.** 34.04 m²   **D.** 12 m²   8. _____

9. Find the volume of a cylinder whose radius is 5.1 cm and whose height is 3.8 cm.
   A. 98.9 cm²   **B.** 231.2 cm²   **C.** 310.4 cm²   **D.** 60.9 cm²   9. _____

10. Find the surface area of a prism with length 7.4 m, width 5.6 m, and height 3.1 m.
    A. 163.5 m²   **B.** 32.2 m²   **C.** 16.1 m²   **D.** 256.9 m²   10. _____

11. Write 55% as a decimal.
    A. 5.5   **B.** 55   **C.** 0.055   **D.** 0.55   11. _____

12. Alberta answered 60 out of 70 questions on her history test correctly. Find the percent of the questions that Alberta answered correctly.
    A. 60%   **B.** 70%   **C.** 86%   **D.** 42%   12. _____

13. Find the purchase price of a $19 hat on sale for 25% off with 7.5% sales tax.
    A. $25.53   **B.** $15.32   **C.** $11.25   **D.** $13.18   13. _____

14. Evaluate $C(6, 4)$.
    A. 30   **B.** 90   **C.** 126   **D.** 15   14. _____

15. If 100 of the 26,000 workers at Happy Valley Farm were selected at random and 69 of them said they liked their job, how many of the workers at Happy Valley would you expect *do not* like their job?
    A. 31   **B.** 8,060   **C.** 839   **D.** 17,940   15. _____

1. A can of corn weighs 12 ounces. Jimmy eats half of the corn in the can for dinner. The can and the corn that is left weigh 7.25 ounces. How much does the can weigh?

   A. 1.66 oz   **B.** 2.5 oz   **C.** 4.75 oz   **D.** 0.6 oz

   1. _____

2. Solve $3x + 1 = -11$.

   A. 4   **B.** -3.3 **C.** -4 **D.** 3

   2. _____

3. Solve $22 - 4n = 3.6$.

   A. -6.4 **B.** -4.6 **C.** 4.6   **D.** 6.4

   3. _____

4. Solve $\frac{2}{3}(s - 3) = 1.2$.

   A. -1.2 **B.** -0.53 **C.** 2.13   **D.** 4.8

   4. _____

5. Find three solutions of the equation $y = x - 3$.

   A. $(-1, -2); (0, 3); (1, 2)$ **B.** $(-1, -4); (0, -3); (1, -2)$
   C. $(-1, 3); (0, 0); (1, 3)$ **D.** $(-1, 4); (0, 3); (1, 4)$

   5. _____

6. Find three solutions of the equation $y = -2x + 1$.

   A. $(-1, -3); (0, -1); (1, -2)$ **B.** $(-1, -1); (0, 1); (1, -1)$
   C. $(-1, 3); (0, 1); (1, -1)$ **D.** $(-1, -2); (0, -1); (1, 0)$

   6. _____

7. Find three solutions of the equation $y = \frac{1}{2}x - 1$.

   A. $(-1, -6); (0, -1); (1, 4)$ **B.** $(-1, -1.5); (0, -1); (1, -0.5)$
   C. $(-1, -0.5); (0, -1); (1, 0.5)$ **D.** $(0, -1); (1, -0.5); (2, -0.75)$

   7. _____

The phone company charges \$1.25 to connect a long-distance telephone call. It also charges \$0.25 for each minute you talk. Use this information for Exercises 8 and 9.

8. Write an equation for the cost of making a long-distance telephone call.

   A. $y = 1.5x + 0.25$ **B.** $y = 1.25x + 0.25$
   C. $y = 0.25x + 1.25$ **D.** $y = 1.5x + 1.25$

   8. _____

9. How much will a 5-minute long-distance telephone call cost.

   A. \$3.00   **B.** \$7.75   **C.** \$6.50   **D.** \$2.50

   9. _____

10. Translate the sentence *the first number is 6 less than two times the second* into an equation.

    A. $y = 2x - 6$ **B.** $y = 6 - 2x$ **C.** $y = 6 + 2x$ **D.** $y = -2x - 6$

    10. _____

11. Translate the sentence *the first number is 1 less than twice the second* into an equation.

    A. $y = 2 - x$ **B.** $y = 2 + x$ **C.** $y = 2x - 1$ **D.** $y = -x - 2$

    11. _____

12. Inga baked a batch of bran cookies. She kept one third of them for herself and donated the rest to the school fair. She packed the cookies for the fair in 8 boxes, a dozen to each box. How many cookies did she bake?
   A. 96   **B.** 343   **C.** 729   **D.** 144

12. _____

Use the graph for Exercises 13 and 14.

13. Which line is the graph of
   $y = x - 2$?
   A. line k
   B. line l
   C. line m
   D. line n

13. _____

14. Which is the graph of $y = -3x - 1$?
   A. line k **B.** line l **C.** line m **D.** line n

14. _____

15. Find the output for the function $f(x) = 3x$ given the input $x = -2, 0, 1, 2$.
   A. 6, 0, 3, 6   **B.** 1, 3, 4, 5   **C.** −5, 0, 3, 5   **D.** −6, 0, 3, 6

15. _____

16. Find the output for the function $f(x) = -2x - 1.5$ given the input $x = -2, -1, 1, 2$.
   A. 2.5, 0.5, −3.5, −5.5   **B.** −2.5, −0.5, −3.5, −5.5
   C. −5.5, −3.5, 0.5, 3.5   **D.** −5.5, −3.5, −3.5, −5.5

16. _____

17. Find the output for the function $f(x) = 0.25x - 2$ given the input $x = -4, 0, 4, 8$.
   A. −1, 0, 1, 2   **B.** 3, 2, 1, 0   **C.** −3, −2, −1, 0   **D.** −4, −2, 0, 2

17. _____

18. Using the graph at the right, which line is the graph of the function $f(x) = -x + 1.5$?
   A. line r
   B. line s
   C. line t
   D. function is not on graph

18. _____

19. Use the graph at the right to describe the movement from $\triangle ABC$ to $\triangle A'B'C'$.
   A. (−5, −7)
   B. (5, 7)
   C. (−7, −5)
   D. (7, 5)

19. _____

20. Use the graph at the right to describe the movement from $\triangle STU$ to $\triangle S'T'U'$.
   A. translation
   B. reflection over the y-axis
   C. reflection over the x-axis
   D. no movement

20. _____

BONUS Which ordered pair describes a reflection over the x-axis and the y-axis?
   A. (−x, y)   **B.** (x, −y)   **C.** (x, y)   **D.** (−x, −y)

_____

Form 1B

1. Mr. Maxwell started three separate bank accounts for his three children, Jerry, Tony, and Nina. He put the same amount of money in each child's account. If Tony withdrew half of his money and spent it all on a $15 CD, how much did Mr. Maxwell deposit in total?

    A. $30   **B.** $90   **C.** $45   **D.** $120

    1. _____

2. Solve $-3m - 21 = -6$.

    A. 5   **B.** -9 **C.** 9   **D.** -5

    2. _____

3. Solve $2y - 1.7 = 3.3$.

    A. -2.5 **B.** 0.8   **C.** 2.5   **D.** -0.8

    3. _____

4. Solve $\frac{1}{5}(t + 2) = 2$.

    A. -1.6 **B.** 12   **C.** 8   **D.** 0

    4. _____

5. Find three solutions of the equation $y = 3x - 1$.

    A. $(-1, -4); (0, -1); (1, 2)$ **B.** $(-1, 4); (0, 1); (1, 2)$
    C. $(-1, 4); (0, -1); (1, 4)$ **D.** $(-1, 1); (0, 2); (1, 3)$

    5. _____

6. Find three solutions of the equation $y = \frac{1}{2}x - 2$.

    A. $(-1, -2.5); (0, -2); (1, -1.5)$
    B. $(-1, 2.5); (0, 2); (1, 1.5)$
    C. $(-1, 1); (0, 0); (1, -1)$
    D. $(-1, -4); (0, -2); (1, 0)$

    6. _____

7. Find three solutions of the equation $y = -5x + 3.5$.

    A. $(-1, -2.5); (0, -1.5); (1, -0.5)$
    B. $(-1, 8.5); (0, 3.5); (1, 1.5)$
    C. $(-1, 1.5); (0, -3.5); (1, -8.5)$
    D. $(-1, 8.5); (0, 3.5); (1, -1.5)$

    7. _____

To mow a lawn, Jessica charges $2 for the use of the equipment plus an additional $3 for every hour it takes her to finish the job. Use this information for Exercises 8 and 9.

8. Write an equation for the cost of mowing a lawn.

    A. $y = 2x + 3$ **B.** $y = 6x$ **C.** $y = 3x + 2$ **D.** $2y = 3x$

    8. _____

9. How much will it cost to have Jessica mow your lawn if it takes her three hours?

    A. $15   **B.** $9   **C.** $11   **D.** $13

    9. _____

10. Translate the sentence *the first number is ten more than one half of the second* into an equation.

    A. $y = 5 + x$ **B.** $y = 0.5x - 10$
    C. $y = 10 - 0.5x$ **D.** $y = 10 + 0.5x$

    10. _____

11. Translate the sentence *the first number is eight less than four times the second* into an equation.

    A. $y = 8 - 4x$ **B.** $y = 8x - 4$ **C.** $y = 4x - 8$ **D.** $y = 4x + 8$

    11. _____

Chapter 14 Test Form 1B continued

12. Mikva baked a batch of ginger cookies. She kept one quarter of them for herself and gave the rest to the school carnival. She packed the cookies for the carnival in 18 boxes, a dozen to a box. How many cookies did she bake?

   A. 1,024   **B.** 288   **C.** 72   **D.** 144

12. _____

Use the graph below to answer Exercises 13 and 14.

13. Which line is the graph of the equation $y = x$?

   A. line k
   B. line l
   C. line m
   D. line n

13. _____

14. Which line is the graph of $y = -x - 4$?

   A. line k **B.** line l **C.** line m **D.** line n

14. _____

15. Find the output for the function $f(x) = 6x$ given the input $x = -3, -2, -1, 0$.

   A. $-9, -8, -7, -6$ **B.** $3, 4, 5, 6$
   C. $18, 12, 6, 0$ **D.** $-18, -12, -6, 0$

15. _____

16. Find the output for the function $f(x) = \frac{1}{2}x + 5$ given the input $x = 0, 1, 2, 3$.

   A. $5, 2.5, 5, 7.5$ **B.** $5, 5.5, 6, 6.5$
   C. $0, 7, 9, 11$ **D.** $0.5, 5.5, 10.5, 15.5$

16. _____

17. Find the output for the function $f(x) = 2x - 3$ given the input $x = -1, 0, 1, 2$.

   A. $1, -3, -1, 1$ **B.** $-5, -3, -1, -1$
   C. $-2, -1, 0, 1$ **D.** $-5, -3, -1, 1$

17. _____

18. Using the graph at the right, which line is the graph of the function $f(x) = 1.5x - 3$?

   A. line r
   B. line s
   C. line t
   D. function not on graph

18. _____

19. Using the graph at the right, describe the movement from $\triangle DEF$ to $\triangle D'E'F'$.

   A. $(5, 2)$
   B. $(-5, 2)$
   C. $(2, -5)$
   D. $(2, 5)$

19. _____

20. Using the graph at the right, describe the movement from $\triangle PQR$ to $\triangle P'Q'R'$.

   A. translation
   B. no movement
   C. reflection over the y-axis
   D. reflection over the x-axis

20. _____

BONUS Solve $4 - 7x = 2x + 1$.

   A. 3   **B.** $\frac{1}{3}$ **C.** $-\frac{1}{3}$ **D.** -3

_____

Chapter 14 Test

Form 2A _____

1. A carton of one dozen eggs weighs 16 ounces. Leslie uses 4 of the eggs to make cookies. The carton and remaining eggs weigh 11 ounces. How much does the carton weigh?

Solve each equation.

2. $-35 = -6b + 1$ 3. $5.3 - 6m = -1.3$ 4. $\frac{3}{4}(p + 2) = 9$

Find four solutions for each equation. Write your solutions as ordered pairs.

5. $y = -3x + 2$ 6. $y = 4x - 3$

7. At a carnival, it costs $3 for admission plus $0.50 for each ride. Write an equation for the cost of rides and admission.

Graph each equation.

8. $y = 2x - 2$ 9. $y = -x + 3$

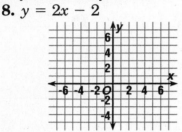 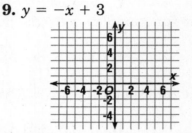

10. Translate the sentence *the first number is 7 less than three times the second number* into an equation.

Find the output for each function, given the input and the function rule.

11. $f(x) = 4x; x = -3, 1, 2, 3.$

12. $f(x) = -3x + 4; x = -4, -2, 0, 2$

13. Graph the function $f(x) = 0.5x - 2.$

Graph each triangle with its transformation. Label all vertices.

14. $\triangle ABC$ with vertices $A(1, 1)$, $B(3, 1)$, and $C(2, 4)$ translated 4 units down and 3 units left

15. $\triangle MNO$ with vertices $M(-4, 2)$, $N(-2, 1)$, and $O(-1, -4)$ reflected over the y-axis.

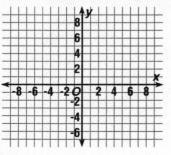 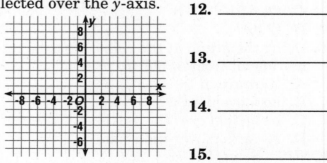

BONUS Solve $6x = -3y + 12$ for $y.$

1. _____

2. _____

3. _____

4. _____

5. _____

6. _____

7. _____

8. _____

9. _____

10. _____

11. _____

12. _____

13. _____

14. _____

15. _____

_____

Glencoe Division, Macmillan/McGraw-Hill

Form 2B

1. Harold, Eugene, and Grace all own an equal number of shares of Anson Stock. Harold sells one fourth of his shares for $3 per share, or a total of $2,100. How many shares of stock did the three own before the sale?

Solve each equation.

2. $-8x + 3 = -29$ 3. $-2.5v - 5 = 4.5$ 4. $\frac{1}{6}(q - 3) = -4$

Find four solutions for each equation. Write your solutions as ordered pairs.

5. $y = 5x - 2$ 6. $y = \frac{1}{2}x + 3$

7. To attract more customers, an office supply store is giving 50 free bonus points to start out, and then one bonus point for every dollar you spend in the store. Write an equation for the number of bonus points you can earn.

Graph each equation.

8. $y = -x + 4$ 9. $y = \frac{1}{2}x - 1$

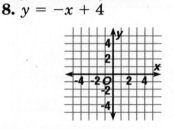 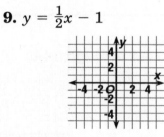

10. Translate the sentence *the first number is five times the second number plus two* into an equation.

Find the output for each function, given the input and the function rule.

11. $f(x) = 5x;\ x = -2, 0, 2, 4$

12. $f(x) = \frac{1}{4}x - 3;\ x = -4, -2, 2, 4$

13. Graph the function $f(x) = 0.5x + 0.5$.

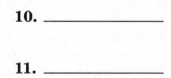

Graph each triangle with its transformation. Label all vertices.

14. $\triangle DEF$ with vertices $D(1, 3)$, $E(4, 1)$, and $F(0, 0)$ translated 3 units left and 1 unit up.

15. $\triangle JKL$ with vertices $J(0, -2)$, $K(2, -1)$, and $L(1, -4)$ reflected over the x-axis.

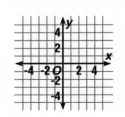

1. _____

2. _____

3. _____

4. _____

5. _____

6. _____

7. _____

8. _____

9. _____

10. _____

11. _____

12. _____

13. _____

14. _____

15. _____

BONUS Solve $21x = 3y + 51$ for y. _____

Chapter 14 Quiz A (Lessons 14-1 through 14-3)

1. Frank stopped his car to fill it with gas since his gas gauge read $\frac{1}{8}$ full. After he put gas in the tank, the gas gauge read $\frac{3}{4}$ full. The pump showed that Frank has put 12.5 gallons into his tank. How much gas was in the tank before Frank put gas in it?

Solve each equation.

2. $5 - 6x = -13$ 3. $3w + 6.9 = 8.4$

Find four solutions for each equation. Write the solutions as ordered pairs.

4. $y = 2x + 3$ 5. $y = \frac{1}{3}x - 3$

1. _____

2. _____

3. _____

4. _____

5. _____

Chapter 14 Quiz B (Lessons 14-4 through 14-6)

1. Graph the equation $y = -x - 3$.

2. Translate the sentence *the first number is two less than negative three times the second* into an equation.

3. Graph the function $y = 2 - x$.

4. Find the output for the function $f(x) = -2x - 4$ given the input $x = 0.5, 1, 1.5, 2$.

5. Graph $\triangle GHI$ with vertices $G(-5, 0)$, $H(-5, 5)$, and $I(-8, -4)$ translated 12 units right and 4 units down.

1. _____

2. _____

3. _____

4. _____

5. _____

Cumulative Review Chapters 1-14

1. Find 0.67×0.3. (Lesson 2-4)

2. Use the divisibility rules to determine if 420 is divisible by 2, 3, 5, 6, 9, or 10. (Lesson 4-1)

3. Find $23 - (-8)$. (Lesson 7-5)

4. Complete the pattern unit for the reflection. (Lesson 8-7)

5. Find the area of a trapezoid whose bases are 13 mm and 14 mm and whose height is 3 mm. (Lesson 9-7)

6. Draw the 3-dimensional figure from the top, front, and side views given. (Lesson 10-1)

   top   front   side

7. Find the volume of a rectangular prism having a length of 15 feet, a width of 10 feet, and a height of 23 feet. (Lesson 10-5)

8. Express 0.00021 as a percent. (Lesson 11-10)

9. Solve $\frac{18}{x} = \frac{25}{14}$. (Lesson 11-3)

10. Louise found a $54 sweater marked down $9. Express this price reduction as a percent. (Lesson 11-8)

11. On a map, the scale is $\frac{1}{8}$ inch:10 miles. Find the actual distance if the map distance is $11\frac{1}{4}$ inches. (Lesson 11-5)

12. Find 85% of 665. (Lesson 12-1)

13. Find the number that is 69% of 46 using the percent equation. (Lesson 12-5)

14. Tim borrowed $2,600 to help pay for his college tuition. The loan was made at 12% interest for 24 months. Find the amount of interest Tim will pay on the loan. (Lesson 12-9)

15. Bob bought 2 button-down shirts, 3 pullover shirts, 2 pairs of socks, and 3 pairs of pants. How many outfits of shirts, pants, and socks can Bob make with his new clothes? (Lesson 13-2)

16. Find $P(4, 2)$. (Lesson 13-7)

17. Out of 20 rolls of a die, Mark rolls a 4 five times. What is the experimental probability of rolling a 4? (Lesson 13-3)

18. Solve $6x - 2 = 19$. (Lesson 14-2)

19. Find four solutions for $y = 2x - 4$. (Lesson 14-3)

20. Find the output for the function $f(x) = 2x + 6$ given the input $x = -2, 0, 1, 2$. (Lesson 14-5)

1. _____
2. _____
3. _____
4. _____
5. _____
6. _____
7. _____
8. _____
9. _____
10. _____
11. _____
12. _____
13. _____
14. _____
15. _____
16. _____
17. _____
18. _____
19. _____
20. _____

Glencoe Division, Macmillan/McGraw-Hill

Cumulative Test Chapters 1-14

1. Multiply 0.023×0.31.   1. _____
   A. 0.00713   B. 0.0713   C. 0.713   D. 0.000713

2. Deetermine if 1,350 is divisible by 2, 3, 5, 6, 9, or 10.   2. _____
   A. 2, 5, 9, 10   B. 3, 5, 9, 10   C. 5, 9, 10   D. 2, 3, 5, 6, 9, 10

3. Complete the pattern unit for the reflection at the right.   3. _____
   A.   B.   C.   D.

4. Find the area of a trapezoid whose bases are 15 yards and 21   4. _____
   yards and whose height is 4.1 yards.
   A. 1291.5 yd^2 B. 147.6 yd^2 C. 73.8 yd^2 D. 645.75 yd^2

5. Find the volume of a rectangular prism having a length of   5. _____
   2.1 inches, a width of 2.5 inches, and a height of 5.5 inches.
   A. 61.1 in^3 B. 20.2 in^3 C. 14.4 in^3 D. 28.875 in^3

6. Express 0.0099 as a percent.   6. _____
   A. 99%   B. 0.099%   C. 0.99%   D. 0.000099%

7. Solve $\frac{x}{42} = \frac{15}{9}$.   7. _____
   A. 25.2   B. 32.1   C. 120   D. 70

8. On a map, the scale is $\frac{1}{2}$ inch:25 miles. Find the actual distance if   8. _____
   the map distance is 5.5 inches.
   A. 137.5 miles   B. 68.75 miles   C. 12.5 miles   D. 275 miles

9. Find 26% of 13.   9. _____
   A. 3.38   B. 0.5   C. 26   D. 50

10. Find the number that is 87% of 62 using the percent equation.   10. _____
    A. 1.4   B. 53.94   C. 71.26   D. 25

11. Find $P(7, 7)$.   11. _____
    A. 5,040   B. 1   C. 823,543   D. 49

12. If 10 fives occur on 50 rolls of a die, what is the experimental   12. _____
    probability?
    A. $\frac{1}{10}$ B. $\frac{1}{25}$ C. $\frac{1}{5}$ D. $\frac{3}{10}$

13. Solve $-8 - 4x = 22$.   13. _____
    A. -7.5 B. 7.5   C. -3.5 D. 3.5

14. Find four solutions for the equation $y = 4x - 2$.   14. _____
    A. $(-1, 6); (0, 2); (1, 2); (2, 6)$ B. $(-1, -6); (0, -2); (1, 2); (2, 6)$
    C. $(-1, 1); (0, 2); (1, 3); (2, 4)$ D. $(-1, 6); (0, 2); (1, -2); (2, -6)$

15. Find the output for the function $f(x) = -3x - 4$ given the input   15. _____
    $x = 0, 1, 2, 3$.
    A. $-7, -6, -5, -4$ B. 4, 1, 2, 5
    C. $-4, -1, 2, 5$ D. $-4, -7, -10, -13$

Semester Test

Chapters 1-7, Form 1

1. Estimate the quotient of 7,898 and 23. Use patterns.   1. _____
   - **A.** 500   **B.** 250   **C.** 450   **D.** 400

2. Evaluate $12 + (58 + 42) \div 25$.   2. _____
   - **A.** 16   **B.** 4.5   **C.** 5   **D.** 20

3. Evaluate $\frac{3a}{2} - b$ if $a = 10$ and $b = 5$.   3. _____
   - **A.** 5   **B.** 10   **C.** 15   **D.** 20

4. Evaluate 3^4.   4. _____
   - **A.** 12   **B.** 7   **C.** 81   **D.** 27

5. Solve $m - 19 = 47$.   5. _____
   - **A.** 25   **B.** 28   **C.** 66   **D.** 2.5

6. Solve $\frac{n}{7} = 12$.   6. _____
   - **A.** 84   **B.** 1.7   **C.** 74   **D.** 2

7. Solve $13p = 117$.   7. _____
   - **A.** 1,521   **B.** 104   **C.** 8   **D.** 9

8. Order 0.6, 0.05, 0.83, and 1.01 from least to greatest.   8. _____
   - **A.** 1.01, 0.83, 0.6, 0.05   **B.** 0.83, 0.05, 0.6, 1.01
   - **C.** 0.05, 0.6, 0.83, 1.01   **D.** 0.05, 0.6, 1.01, 0.83

9. Round 3.8<u>5</u>61 to the underlined place-value position.   9. _____
   - **A.** 3.90   **B.** 3.86   **C.** 3.8560   **D.** 3.850

10. Estimate 3.91×52.8. Use an appropriate strategy.   10. _____
    - **A.** 2,000   **B.** 20,000   **C.** 20   **D.** 200

11. Divide $0.097 \overline{)0.425}$. Round to the nearest hundredth.   11. _____
    - **A.** 4.38   **B.** 4.83   **C.** 48.3   **D.** 43.8

12. Write 3.02×10^4 in standard form.   12. _____
    - **A.** 302,000   **B.** 3,020   **C.** 30,200   **D.** 302

13. Complete $0.96L = \blacksquare$ mL.   13. _____
    - **A.** 96,000   **B.** 960   **C.** 9,600   **D.** 96

14. A giant tortoise can travel at about 0.4 kilometers per hour. At this rate, how far can it travel in 3 hours 30 minutes?   14. _____
    - **A.** 1.4 km   **B.** 1.2 km   **C.** 2.6 km   **D.** 3.0 km

15. Find the range of 10, 11, 9, 15, 14, 12, and 13.   15. _____
    - **A.** 12   **B.** 11   **C.** 6   **D.** 13

Semester Test Chapters 1–7, Form 1 continued

Use the line plot to answer Exercises 16–17.

16. Name the outlier in the line plot.
   A. 20   **B.** 28   **C.** 24   **D.** 22

```
            ×
            ×    ×    ×
     ×      ×    ×    ×
  ×         ×    ×    ×
  +--+--+--+--+--+--+-->
  20 22 24 26 28 30
```

17. Name the cluster in the line plot.
   A. between 20 and 24   **B.** between 20 and 28
   C. between 24 and 28   **D.** between 20 and 26

16. _____

17. _____

The stem-and-leaf plot shows the scores on a mathematics test.
Use this plot to answer Exercises 18–21.

```
5 | 024
6 | 122
7 | 27888
8 | 14799
9 | 348
```

18. Find the mode.
   A. 77   **B.** 78
   C. 79   **D.** 80

18. _____

19. Find the median.
   A. 79   **B.** 80   **C.** 78   **D.** 77

19. _____

20. Find the mean. Round to the nearest tenth.
   A. 75.7   **B.** 78.3   **C.** 76.9   **D.** 79.2

20. _____

21. If 60 is the lowest passing score, how many scores are passing?
   A. 13   **B.** 14   **C.** 16   **D.** 3

21. _____

22. Find the prime factorization of 69.
   A. $2 \cdot 3 \cdot 7$ **B.** $3 \cdot 3 \cdot 7$ **C.** $5 \cdot 19$ **D.** $3 \cdot 23$

22. _____

23. Find the next term in the sequence 71, 64, 57, 50, ...
   A. 56   **B.** 50   **C.** 75   **D.** 43

23. _____

24. Find the sixth term in the sequence 64, 16, 4, 1, ...
   A. $\frac{1}{16}$ **B.** $\frac{1}{4}$ **C.** 4   **D.** 16

24. _____

25. Find the LCM and GCF of 18 and 36.
   A. 36; 9   **B.** 9; 36   **C.** 36; 18   **D.** 18; 36

25. _____

26. Express $\frac{51}{68}$ in simplest form.
   A. $\frac{2}{3}$ **B.** $\frac{3}{4}$ **C.** $\frac{4}{9}$ **D.** $\frac{5}{6}$

26. _____

27. Express 0.375 as a fraction in simplest form.
   A. $\frac{1}{6}$ **B.** $\frac{2}{3}$ **C.** $\frac{3}{8}$ **D.** $\frac{5}{8}$

27. _____

A bag contains 3 blue, 4 red, 2 green, and 6 white marbles.
If you draw a marble at random:

28. What is the probability of drawing a blue marble?
   A. $\frac{4}{15}$ **B.** $\frac{1}{3}$ **C.** $\frac{1}{5}$ **D.** $\frac{2}{3}$

28. _____

29. What is probability of drawing a marble that is not white?
   A. $\frac{3}{5}$ **B.** $\frac{1}{5}$ **C.** $\frac{4}{5}$ **D.** $\frac{2}{15}$

29. _____

Semester Test Chapters 1–7, Form 1 continued

30. Estimate $8\frac{1}{5} - 3\frac{7}{8}$.   30. _____

   A. 5   **B.** 6   **C.** 3   **D.** 4

Solve each equation. Write each solution in simplest form.

31. $a = \frac{5}{8} - \frac{2}{5}$ 31. _____

   A. $\frac{3}{13}$ **B.** 1   **C.** $\frac{9}{40}$ **D.** $\frac{25}{16}$

32. $b = 1\frac{3}{4} \div \frac{7}{8}$ 32. _____

   A. $\frac{5}{4}$ **B.** 2   **C.** $3\frac{1}{2}$ **D.** 3

33. Find the perimeter of a square with a side of $2\frac{2}{3}$ yards.   33. _____

   A. 6 yd   **B.** $11\frac{1}{3}$ yd   **C.** $10\frac{2}{3}$ yd   **D.** $5\frac{1}{3}$ yd

34. Find the circumference of a circle whose radius is 1.25 feet.   34. _____

   A. 7.85 ft   **B.** 4.875 ft   **C.** 6.125 ft   **D.** 3.925 ft

35. The spinner tells the number of dollars you win. Find the expected value of a spin.   35. _____

   A. $2.25   **B.** $2.00
   C. $2.75   **D.** $3.00

36. In Exercise 35, over the long-term, would you expect to win, lose, or break even if each spin cost $2?   36. _____

   A. win   **B.** lose   **C.** break even   **D.** none

37. A taxi charges $1.25 for the first $\frac{1}{5}$ mile and 50¢ for each additional $\frac{1}{5}$ mile. Estimate the cost of a 6-mile ride?   37. _____

   A. $14   **B.** $16   **C.** $19   **D.** $20

38. Solve $x + 13.9 = 15.2$.   38. _____

   A. 211.3   **B.** 211   **C.** 1.3   **D.** 29.1

39. Solve $\frac{z}{0.7} = 1.5$.   39. _____

   A. 2.2   **B.** 1.05   **C.** 0.8   **D.** 2.14

40. Translate *the product of 8 and t* into an algebraic expression.   40. _____

   A. $8 + t$ **B.** $8 - t$ **C.** $8 \div t$ **D.** $8t$

41. How many quarts are in $6\frac{1}{2}$ gallons?   41. _____

   A. 26   **B.** 13   **C.** 12   **D.** 24

42. Find the area of a parallelogram with a base of 2.5 meters and a height of 3.6 meters.   42. _____

   A. 12.2 m^2 **B.** 10.1 m^2 **C.** 7.1 m^2 **D.** 9 m^2

43. What is the length of a rectangle with an area of 10.53 square kilometers and a width of 2.7 kilometers?   43. _____

   A. 4.8 km   **B.** 3.9 km   **C.** 4 km   **D.** 6.2 km

Semester Test Chapters 1–7, Form 1 continued

Use the graph to find the ordered pair for each point.

44. Q

   A. $(3, -2)$ **B.** $(-3, -2)$

   C. $(3, 2)$ **D.** $(-3, 2)$

45. E

   A. $(1, -4)$ **B.** $(1, 4)$

   C. $(4, 1)$ **D.** $(4, -1)$

44. _____

45. _____

Solve each equation.

46. $a = 14 - 23$

   A. 9 **B.** 37 **C.** -37 **D.** -9

47. $x = (-63) \div 9$

   A. -7 **B.** -72 **C.** 72 **D.** 7

48. $\frac{c}{3} = -9$

   A. 27 **B.** -3 **C.** -27 **D.** 3

49. Write 0.000027 in scientific notation.

   A. 2.7×10^{-5} **B.** 27×10^{-4}

   C. 2.7×10^{-4} **D.** 27×10^{-5}

50. Write an equation for the following. Then solve.
If you decrease a number by 6, the result is -13.

   A. $n - 6 = -13; n = -7$

   B. $n + 6 = -13; n = -19$

   C. $6n = -13; n = -\frac{13}{6}$

   D. $n \div 6 = -13; n = -78$

46. _____

47. _____

48. _____

49. _____

50. _____

Semester Test

Chapters 1–7, Form 2

1. Estimate $4{,}199 \div 7$. Use compatible numbers.

2. Evaluate $(29 - 17) \div 4 + 8$.

3. Evaluate $3(b + c) - a$ if $a = 8$, $b = 7$, and $c = 5$.

4. Evaluate 9^3.

5. Solve $54 = r - 26$.

6. Solve $17t = 119$.

7. Three girls share a large pizza. The medium size costs $8. The large size costs more than the medium size. How much did each girl pay?

8. Order 2.53, 2.74, 0.91, and 0.9 from greatest to least.

9. Round 3.46<u>8</u>2 to the underlined place-value position.

10. Estimate 31.7×48.9. Use an appropriate strategy.

11. Write 7.61×10^5 in standard form.

12. Complete $415\text{g} = \blacksquare$ kg.

13. Divide $0.06\overline{)0.0571}$. Round to the nearest hundredth.

14. Courtney works 15 hours a week and earns $5.50 an hour. How much does she earn in three weeks?

15. Frank's golf scores for five rounds were 78, 74, 76, 70, and 80. Find an appropriate scale and interval. Draw a number line to show them.

16. Make a line plot for the data 24, 26, 24, 26, 27, 26, and 23.

17. Find the range, mode, median, and mean for the data in Exercise 16.

18. Make a stem-and-leaf plot for the data 31, 27, 42, 24, 27, 23, 32, 46, 13, and 35.

19. At IBX Rental, 6 employees earn $30,000, 3 earn $42,000, and 2 earn $72,500. List the salaries on the frequency table at the right.

Salary	Frequency

20. Find the mode, the median, and the mean of the salaries in Exercise 19.

1. _____

2. _____

3. _____

4. _____

5. _____

6. _____

7. _____

8. _____

9. _____

10. _____

11. _____

12. _____

13. _____

14. _____

15. _____

16. _____

17. _____

18. _____

19. _____

_____

20. _____

Semester Test Chapters 1–7, Form 2 continued

21. Which number would you use to best describe the salaries in Exercise 19: mode, median, or mean? Explain.

21. _____

22. Determine whether 3,240 is divisible by 2, 3, 4, 5, 6, 9, or 10.

22. _____

23. Identify the sequence 2, 8, 32, 128, . . . as arithmetic, geometric, or neither. Then find the next three terms in the sequence.

23. _____

24. Find the GCF and LCM of 24 and 36.

24. _____

25. Write $\frac{32}{48}$ in simplest form.

25. _____

26. Express $\frac{6}{11}$ as a decimal. Use bar notation if necessary.

26. _____

The spinner shown at the right is equally likely to stop on each of the regions. Find the probability that the spinner will stop on:

27. a prime number

27. _____

28. an even number

28. _____

29. A condominium rents for $850 a month. The monthly rent is expected to increase $30 each year. How much will the monthly rent be at the end of 5 years?

29. _____

30. Estimate $10\frac{1}{8} \div 4\frac{5}{6}$.

30. _____

31. Solve $\frac{8}{9} + \frac{5}{6} = a$. Write the solution in simplest form.

31. _____

32. Solve $b = \frac{11}{12} \times \frac{4}{33}$. Write the solution in simplest form.

32. _____

33. Subtract $14\frac{3}{7} - 8\frac{11}{21}$. Write the solution in simplest form.

33. _____

34. Find the perimeter of a rectangle with $l = 5\frac{1}{2}$ yards and $w = 3\frac{3}{4}$ yards.

34. _____

35. Find the circumference of a circle whose diameter is $\frac{3}{4}$ foot. Use $\pi \approx 3.14$.

35. _____

36. The spinner shown at the right tells the number of dollars you win. Over the long run, would you expect to win, lose, or break even if each spin costs $3?

36. _____

37. Solve $z + 5.6 = 13.4$ by using the inverse operation.

37. _____

Semester Test Chapters 1–7, Form 2 continued

Solve each equation by using properties of equality. Check your solution.

38. $10\frac{1}{2} = m - 4\frac{2}{3}$

39. $\frac{1}{4}n = \frac{7}{12}$

40. Translate *thirteen more than k* into an algebraic expression.

Find the area of each figure.

41.

rectangle | 1.7 cm

3.4 cm

42.

25 mm   17 mm

39 mm

43. A number is multiplied by 9. Then 15 is added to the result. If the result is 51, what was the original number?

On the coordinate plane, graph and label each point.

44. $P(0, -3)$

45. $Q(-2, -3)$

Solve each equation.

46. $\frac{x}{-4} = 7$

47. $-13y = -52$

48. $-4 = w - 9$

49. Write 0.00000063 in scientific notation.

50. Jeff did 8 sit-ups on the first day. Then each day after that he did 9, 11, 14, 18, and 23 sit-ups. If he follows the same pattern, how many sit-ups should he do on the eighth day?

38. _____

39. _____

40. _____

41. _____

42. _____

43. _____

44. _____

45. _____

46. _____

47. _____

48. _____

49. _____

50. _____

Final Test

Form 1 ━━━━━━━━━━━━━━━━━━━━━━━━━━━━━

1. Evaluate $16(3 - 1) \div 4 + 4$.   1. _____
  A. 15.75   **B.** 4   **C.** 12   **D.** 20

2. Solve $13b = 117$.   2. _____
  A. 130   **B.** 104   **C.** 1,521   **D.** 9

3. Write 29,000,000 in scientific notation.   3. _____
  A. 2.9×10^6 **B.** 2.9×10^7
  C. 2.9×10^8 **D.** 0.29×10^8

4. Round 3.58043 to the nearest thousandth.   4. _____
  A. 3.6   **B.** 3.58   **C.** 3.580   **D.** 3.5804

5. Which number would *not* appear as a leaf when drawing a   5. _____
  stem-and-leaf plot of the data 90, 82, 76, 96, 88, 74, 77, 95,
  and 75?
  A. 3   **B.** 4   **C.** 5   **D.** 6

6. Find the median of 43, 37, 46, 37, 38, 40, and 42.   6. _____
  A. 37   **B.** 40.4   **C.** 40   **D.** 42

7. Find the GCF of 78 and 130.   7. _____
  A. 2   **B.** 13   **C.** 4   **D.** 26

8. Find the sixth term in the sequence 83, 77, 71, 65, ...   8. _____
  A. 59   **B.** 29   **C.** 53   **D.** 47

9. Express $\frac{24}{88}$ as a fraction in simplest form.   9. _____
  A. $\frac{12}{44}$ **B.** $\frac{3}{11}$ **C.** $\frac{6}{22}$ **D.** $\frac{1}{3}$

10. Find $\frac{8}{9} \div 1\frac{5}{27}$.   10. _____
  A. $\frac{4}{3}$ **B.** $\frac{3}{4}$ **C.** $\frac{8}{27}$ **D.** $\frac{5}{8}$

11. Find $\frac{5}{9} - \frac{1}{12}$.   11. _____
  A. $\frac{4}{3}$ **B.** $\frac{5}{108}$ **C.** $\frac{20}{3}$ **D.** $\frac{17}{36}$

12. Solve $d - 2.4 = 13.8$.   12. _____
  A. 11.4   **B.** 5.75   **C.** 33.12   **D.** 16.2

Final Test, Form 1 continued

13. Find the perimeter of a square with sides of $2\frac{2}{3}$ feet.   13. _____
    A. $10\frac{2}{3}$ feet   **B.** $8\frac{2}{3}$ feet   **C.** $\frac{8}{9}$ feet   **D.** $9\frac{1}{3}$ feet

14. Change 2.25 pounds to ounces.   14. _____
    A. 36 oz   **B.** 18 oz   **C.** 4.5 oz   **D.** 54 oz

15. What is the length of a rectangle with an area of 16.2 square   15. _____
    centimeters and a width of 5.4 centimeters?
    A. 12.4 cm   **B.** 2.7 cm   **C.** 3 cm   **D.** 87.48 cm

16. Order 2, −1, 0, −2, and −4 from least to greatest.   16. _____
    A. 0, 1, −2, 2, −4   **B.** −1, −2, 0, 2, −4
    C. −2, −1, 0, 1, −4   **D.** −4, −2, −1, 0, 2

17. Solve $-2 - 2 = c$.   17. _____
    A. −4   **B.** 4   **C.** 0   **D.** 1

18. Solve $3 = y - 6$.   18. _____
    A. −9   **B.** −3   **C.** 3   **D.** 9

19. Write 0.0037 in scientific notation.   19. _____
    A. 3.7×10^{-3} **B.** 3.7×10^{3}
    C. 3.7×10^{-4} **D.** 0.37×10^{-4}

20. The measure of an angle is 180°. Classify the angle.   20. _____
    A. acute   **B.** obtuse   **C.** right   **D.** straight

21. Which figure is a polygon?   21. _____
    A.   **B.**   **C.**   **D.**

22. Classify a polygon having seven sides.   22. _____
    A. hexagon   **B.** nonagon
    C. heptagon   **D.** decagon

23. Which regular polygon can be used by itself to make a   23. _____
    tessellation?
    A. heptagon   **B.** triangle
    C. pentagon   **D.** octagon

24. Complete the pattern unit for a reflection that is   24. _____
    shown at the right.
    A.   **B.**   **C.**   **D.**

25. Find the square root of 256.   25. _____
    A. 30   **B.** 128   **C.** 16   **D.** 12

26. Estimate $\sqrt{19}$.   26. _____
    A. 4   **B.** 5   **C.** 8   **D.** 9

Final Test, Form 1 continued

27. Use the Pythagorean Theorem to find the length of the hypo-   **27.** _____
tenuse of a right triangle if its legs measure 3 yards and
8 yards.
  A. 7.4 yards   **B.** 8.5 yards
  C. 11 yards   **D.** 4.9 yards

28. Find the area of a triangle whose base is 6.2 meters and whose   **28.** _____
height is 9.8 meters.
  A. 30.38 m^2 **B.** 60.76 m^2 **C.** 8 m^2 **D.** 11.6 m^2

29. Find the area of a trapezoid whose bases are 1 mile and 5 miles   **29.** _____
and whose height is 3 miles.
  A. 9 mi^2 **B.** 7.5 mi^2 **C.** 6 mi^2 **D.** 18 mi^2

30. Find the radius of a circle that has an area of 34 ft^2.   **30.** _____
  A. 10.83 feet   **B.** 3.29 feet
  C. 5.83 feet   **D.** 10.33 feet

31. Find the surface area of a rectangular prism with a length of   **31.** _____
6 meters, a width of 6 meters, and a height of 9 meters.
  A. 324 m^2 **B.** 288 m^2 **C.** 144 m^2 **D.** 42 m^2

32. Find the surface area of a cylinder whose diameter is 6 meters   **32.** _____
and whose height is 10 meters. Use 3.14 for π.
  A. 602.88 m^2 **B.** 244.92 m^2 **C.** 1,130.4 m^2 **D.** 282.6 m^2

33. Find the volume of a rectangular prism with a length of   **33.** _____
3.1 feet, a width of 2.4 feet, and a height of 4.8 feet.
  A. 10.3 ft^3 **B.** 20.6 ft^3 **C.** 35.712 ft^3 **D.** 224.27 ft^3

34. Find the volume of a cylinder whose radius is 3 inches and   **34.** _____
whose height is 6 inches. Use 3.14 for π.
  A. 169.56 in^3 **B.** 339.12 in^3
  C. 113.04 in^3 **D.** 56.52 in^3

35. A swimming pool that is 65 feet long, 50 feet wide, and 12 feet   **35.** _____
deep is filled to a level of 10 feet. How much water is in the pool?
  A. 195,000 ft^3 **B.** 137 ft^3
  C. 39,000 ft^3 **D.** 32,500 ft^3

36. Write an expression for the volume of cube that has sides y units   **36.** _____
long.
  A. $3y$ **B.** y^2 **C.** y^3 **D.** $3y^2$

37. Write the ratio 39:52 in simplest form.   **37.** _____
  A. 39:52   **B.** 1:18   **C.** 3:4   **D.** 78:104

38. Find the unit price for one dozen eggs priced at $0.96.   **38.** _____
  A. 0.08¢ per egg   **B.** 8¢ per egg
  C. 9.6¢ per egg   **D.** $0.96¢ per egg

Final Test, Form 1 continued

39. Find x in the pair of similar polygons.　　9 yd　5 yd　　**39.** _____
　　A. 0.6 yd　　**B.** 4.7 yd　　　　　x yd　3 yd
　　C. 5.4 yd　　**D.** 7 yd

40. Alexis has a batting average of 0.322. Write this number as a　　**40.** _____
　　percent.
　　A. 322%　　**B.** 32.2%　　**C.** 0.322%　　**D.** 3.22%

41. Write a percent to represent　　**41.** _____
　　the shaded area at the right.
　　A. 40%
　　B. 42%
　　C. 58%
　　D. 60%

42. Express 44% as a fraction in simplest form.　　**42.** _____
　　A. $\frac{11}{25}$　　**B.** $\frac{22}{50}$　　**C.** $\frac{44}{100}$　　**D.** $\frac{1}{44}$

43. Use a proportion to find what number is 62% of 350.　　**43.** _____
　　A. 564.5　　**B.** 5.6　　**C.** 217　　**D.** 17.7

44. On an average day, 350 women and 250 men shop in one　　**44.** _____
　　supermarket. What percent of the shoppers are men?
　　A. 58%　　**B.** 42%　　**C.** 71%　　**D.** 140%

45. Write an equation and solve to find what percent of 8 is 12.　　**45.** _____
　　A. 96%　　**B.** 67%　　**C.** 0.96%　　**D.** 150%

Larry wants to buy a shirt that costs $29.95. Use this information
to answer Exercises 46 and 47.

46. If the shirt is on sale for 20% off, how much will Larry pay for　　**46.** _____
　　the shirt?
　　A. $5.99　　**B.** $23.96　　**C.** $35.94　　**D.** $22.46

47. If the shirt is not on sale and there is 5.5% sales tax, how　　**47.** _____
　　much will Larry have to pay for the shirt?
　　A. $28.30　　**B.** $16.47　　**C.** $31.60　　**D.** $25.28

48. How much interest will be earned after 6 months on a savings　　**48.** _____
　　account containing $250 earning 7% interest annually?
　　A. $105　　**B.** $8.75　　**C.** $10.50　　**D.** $87.50

49. Use a tree diagram to find the number of ways to arrange the　　**49.** _____
　　numbers 2, 4, and 9.
　　A. 15　　**B.** 72　　**C.** 9　　**D.** 6

50. Kim has three V-neck sweaters, two crew neck sweaters, two　　**50.** _____
　　pairs of jeans, two pairs of dress pants, four pairs of knee socks
　　and one pair of bobby socks. How many outfits of sweaters,
　　pants, and socks can Kim make?
　　A. 100　　**B.** 96　　**C.** 14　　**D.** 97

137

Final Test, Form 1 continued

51. Find the probability of rolling one 6 and one 3 when 2 fair dice are rolled.

    A. $\frac{1}{36}$ **B.** $\frac{2}{9}$ **C.** $\frac{1}{9}$ **D.** $\frac{1}{18}$

51. _____

52. A bag contains 9 red, 6 white, 3 blue, and 8 green marbles. Two marbles are drawn, but the first marble drawn is not replaced. Find P(white, then white).

    A. $\frac{3}{65}$ **B.** $\frac{35}{338}$ **C.** $\frac{6}{125}$ **D.** $\frac{9}{169}$

52. _____

53. Find $P(7, 4)$.

    A. 5,040   **B.** 840   **C.** 210   **D.** 35

53. _____

54. How many ways can a nine-member council make its decisions if decisions are made by a majority vote?

    A. 362,880   **B.** 120   **C.** 126   **D.** 15,120

54. _____

55. Solve $3t - 4 = -19$.

    A. $7\frac{2}{3}$ **B.** $-7\frac{2}{3}$ **C.** 5   **D.** -5

55. _____

56. To develop a roll of film, a film developer charges $2 plus $0.25 for each picture developed. How much will it cost to get a roll of 24 pictures developed?

    A. $48.25   **B.** $54   **C.** $8   **D.** $9

56. _____

57. Which line is the graph of the equation $y = 4x + 1$?

    A. line q
    B. line r
    C. line s
    D. line t

57. _____

58. Find the output for the function $f(x) = 0.5x - 6$ given the input $x = -2, 0, 2,$ and 4.

    A. $-7, -6, -5, -4$ **B.** $7, 6, 5, 4$
    C. $7, -6, -5, -4$ **D.** $-16, -6, 4, 14$

58. _____

59. Which line is the graph of the function $f(x) = 1.5x - 3$?

    A. line a
    B. line b
    C. line c
    D. function is not on graph

59. _____

60. Triangle FGH with vertices $F(3, 5)$, $G(5, -1)$ and $H(1, 2)$ is reflected over the y-axis. Write the ordered pairs for the vertices of the new triangle.

    A. $(-3, -5), (-5, 1), (-1, -2)$ **B.** $(3, -5), (5, 1), (1, -2)$
    C. $(3, 5), (5, -1), (1, 2)$ **D.** $(-3, 5), (-5, -1), (-1, 2)$

60. _____

Final Test

Form 2

1. Evaluate $ab + c$ if $a = 3$, $b = 2$, and $c = 7$.

2. Evaluate 3^3.

3. Order 0.37, 0.03, 3.4, and 0.32 from least to greatest.

4. How many nickels are there in $19.50?

5. Find the mean of 2, 4, 7, 5, 8, 0, 6, and 8.

6. Find the range of 38, 55, 91, 92, 34, and 87.

7. Find the LCM of 12, 24, and 30.

8. Find the next term in the sequence 81, 27, 9, 3, ...

9. Find $\frac{4}{7} \times 2\frac{5}{8}$.

10. Find the circumference of a circle whose diameter is $\frac{3}{4}$ yard. Use $\frac{22}{7}$ for π.

11. Solve $r \div \frac{1}{2} = 6$.

12. How many quarts are in 4.25 gallons?

13. Find the area of a parallelogram with a base of 6.2 meters and a height of 9.3 meters.

14. Name the integer represented by R. Then find its opposite and absolute value.

$$R$$
$$\begin{array}{c} \leftarrow\!+\!+\!+\!\bullet\!+\!+\!+\!+\!+\!+\!+\!+\!+\!\rightarrow \\ \text{-6 \quad -4 \quad -2 \quad 0 \quad 2 \quad 4 \quad 6} \end{array}$$

15. Solve $-64 \div (-16) = a$.

16. Write 5×10^{-4} in standard form.

17. Classify an angle of 83° as acute, obtuse, right, or straight.

18. Classify a polygon having 5 sides.

19. Classify triangle X by its sides and its angles.

1. _____
2. _____
3. _____
4. _____
5. _____
6. _____
7. _____
8. _____
9. _____
10. _____
11. _____
12. _____
13. _____
14. _____
15. _____
16. _____
17. _____
18. _____
19. _____

Final Test, Form 2 continued

20. Complete the pattern unit at the right for a translation.

20. _____

21. Find the best whole number estimate for $\sqrt{53}$.

21. _____

22. Is a triangle having sides of lengths 3 inches, 6 inches, and 7 inches a right triangle?

22. _____

23. Find the area of a trapezoid with bases 7 centimeters and 12 centimeters and with height 9 centimeters.

23. _____

24. Find the area of a circle with diameter 5.5 millimeters. Use 3.14 for π.

24. _____

25. Find the base of a triangle whose height is 1.7 feet and whose area is 1.87 ft^2.

25. _____

26. Draw the three dimensional figure by using the top, front, and side views at the right.

front   side   top

26. _____

27. Find the surface area of a cylinder whose height is 15 inches and whose radius is 1 foot. Use 3.14 for π.

27. _____

28. Find the volume of a rectangular prism whose length is 5 feet, width is 7 feet, and height is 3 feet.

28. _____

29. Find the volume of a cylinder with a diameter of 2 inches and a height of 14 inches. Use 3.14 for π.

29. _____

30. A can of tennis balls has a height of 12 inches and a radius of 1.5 inches. What is the volume of the can? Use 3.14 for π.

30. _____

31. Solve the proportion $\frac{5}{t} = \frac{12}{15}$.

31. _____

32. Express 18 people in 4 cars as a unit rate.

32. _____

33. Write the number that is 19% of 70.

33. _____

34. Luis has a field goal percentage of 54.5%. Express this number as a decimal.

34. _____

35. Express the number $\frac{6}{800}$ as a percent.

35. _____

36. Find 72% of 1,150.

36. _____

37. At Great Heights Middle School, there are 30 basketball players, 7 wrestlers, 12 volleyball players, and 20 baseball players. What percent of these athletes are wrestlers? Round your answer to the nearest whole percent.

37. _____

Final Test, Form 2 continued

Bill wants to buy a pair of pants for $19.95. Use this
information to answer Exercises 38 and 39.

38. If the pants are on sale for 30% off, how much will Bill
pay for the pants?

38. _____

39. If the pants are not on sale and there is a 6.25% sales
tax, how much will Bill pay for the pants?

39. _____

40. Find the interest to the nearest cent on a principal of
$1,000 borrowed at a rate of 12.5% annually for 3 years.

40. _____

41. Ngyen has 1 spring coat, 1 winter coat, 2 pairs of
corduroy pants, 3 pairs of jeans, 3 sweaters, and 2 pairs
of gloves. How many different outfits of sweaters, pants,
coats, and gloves can Ngyen make?

41. _____

42. Find the probability of flipping a fair coin and rolling a
fair die at the same time and getting a tail and a 4.

42. _____

43. A bag contains 5 red, 5 white, 5 blue, and 5 green
marbles. Two marbles are drawn, but the first marble
drawn is not replaced. Find P(red, then blue).

43. _____

44. In how many ways can you seat 6 people in 4 chairs?

44. _____

45. Find $C(9, 3)$.

45. _____

46. Solve $-2 - 3y = 22$.

46. _____

47. A carpenter charges $20 for an estimate plus an
additional $25 an hour she works. How much will it cost
you to have 6 hours of work done?

47. _____

48. Graph the equation $y = \frac{1}{3}x - 2$.

48. _____

49. Find the output for the function
$f(x) = 2x - 3$ given the input
$x = -2, 0, 1,$ and 2.

49. _____

50. Graph $\triangle MNR$ with vertices
$M(-5, 4)$, $N(-2, 2)$, and
$R(-3, 0)$ translated 5 units
right and 2 units down.

50. _____

Answer Keys, Chapter 1 Tests and Quizzes

Page 1
Form 1A
Answers

1. __C__
2. __C__
3. __A__
4. __B__
5. __C__
6. __A__
7. __B__
8. __D__
9. __A__
10. __B__
11. __C__
12. __A__
13. __D__
14. __B__
15. __D__

Page 2
Form 1A
Answers

16. __C__
17. __B__
18. __A__
19. __D__
20. __B__
21. __A__
22. __B__
23. __D__
24. __D__
25. __B__
__B__

Page 3
Form 1B
Answers

1. __B__
2. __A__
3. __C__
4. __A__
5. __C__
6. __B__
7. __A__
8. __A__
9. __C__
10. __D__
11. __A__
12. __A__
13. __B__
14. __A__

Page 4
Form 1B
Answers

15. __B__
16. __D__
17. __D__
18. __C__
19. __A__
20. __B__
21. __C__
22. __D__
23. __B__
24. __C__
25. __A__
__D__

Glencoe Division, Macmillan/McGraw-Hill

Page 5
Form 2A
Answers

1. 4,000
2. 18,000
3. 14,000
4. 4,000
5. 200
6. 180,000
7. yes
8. yes
9. no
10. yes
11. 12
12. 20
13. 6
14. 34
15. $7 \cdot 7 \cdot 7 \cdot 7$
16. 11^2
17. 10,000
18. 81
19. 9
20. 167
21. 88
22. 154
23. No
24. 199
25. $63.80
    $\frac{1}{3}$

Page 6
Form 2B
Answers

1. 12,000
2. 18,000
3. 14,000
4. 5,000
5. 54,000
6. 90
7. no
8. yes
9. yes
10. yes
11. 1
12. 13
13. 8
14. 10
15. $6 \cdot 6 \cdot 6 \cdot 6$
16. 11^4
17. 1,728
18. 16
19. 100
20. 9
21. 39
22. 105
23. $5.30
24. about 55 m
25. The costs are missing.
    6

Page 7
Quiz A
Answers

1. 6,000
2. 15,000
3. 72,000
4. 20
5. yes
6. no
7. no
8. yes
9. yes
10. $28.25

Quiz B
Answers

Quiz B
Answers

1. 19
2. 0
3. 1
4. 31
5. $8 \cdot 8 \cdot 8 \cdot 8 \cdot 8$
6. 25^2
7. 16
8. 30
9. 24
10. Price for solid socks is missing.

Page 8
Cumulative Review
Answers

1. 5,000
2. 17,000
3. 13,000
4. 4,000
5. 100
6. 32,000
7. no
8. no
9. no
10. yes
11. 12
12. 2
13. 16
14. 6
15. $8 \cdot 8 \cdot 8$
16. 3^5
17. 2,401
18. 25
19. 8
20. 101
21. 82
22. 204
23. No
24. 1,312
25. $179.40

Page 9
Cumulative Test
Answers

1. D
2. D
3. C
4. B
5. B
6. B
7. A
8. D
9. C
10. A
11. B
12. A
13. C
14. B
15. A
16. A
17. D
18. B
19. C
20. A
21. A
22. B
23. D
24. B
25. D

Glencoe Division, Macmillan/McGraw-Hill

Answer Keys, Chapter 2 Tests and Quizzes

Page 10
Form 1A
Answers

1. __B__
2. __C__
3. __D__
4. __A__
5. __B__
6. __C__
7. __D__
8. __D__
9. __A__
10. __D__
11. __A__
12. __C__
13. __A__
14. __C__

Page 11
Form 1A
Answers

15. __D__
16. __A__
17. __B__
18. __C__
19. __A__
20. __B__
21. __D__
22. __A__
23. __B__
24. __D__
25. __C__

__A__

Page 12
Form 1B
Answers

1. __A__
2. __A__
3. __D__
4. __D__
5. __B__
6. __B__
7. __A__
8. __C__
9. __C__
10. __D__
11. __A__
12. __B__
13. __C__
14. __A__

Page 13
Form 1B
Answers

15. __B__
16. __D__
17. __B__
18. __D__
19. __A__
20. __C__
21. __B__
22. __D__
23. __B__
24. __D__
25. __D__

__A__

Glencoe Division, Macmillan/McGraw-Hill

Page 14
Form 2A
Answers

1. 0.68, 0.7, 0.99, 1.01
2. 1.173, 10.006, 10.4, 10.44
3. 215.02
4. 0.7
5. 10
6. 3.1
7. about 16
8. about 3
9. about 1,500
10. about 0.2
11. 39,000
12. 0.0192
13. 2,900
14. 9
15. 450
16. 4,090
17. 7.95×10^2
18. 2,930
19. 0.432
20. 2.13
21. about $120
22. 5.8 L
23. 35¢
24. 17.3 mi
25. $15
    15,570

Page 15
Form 2B
Answers

1. 0.9, 0.91, 1.53, 1.74
2. 6.0, 6.01, 6.55, 7.032, 7.501
3. 86
4. 0.12
5. 6.2
6. 2.569
7. about 32
8. about 18
9. about 1,200
10. about 0.3
11. 160,000
12. 0.0235
13. 303,000
14. 12
15. 700
16. 890,000
17. 2.14×10^2
18. 0.301
19. 750
20. 5.56
21. about $100
22. 0.75 L
23. $126
24. 54.5 cm
25. $868
    2.9929×10^{26}

Page 16
Quiz A
Answers

1. <
2. >
3. 1.0
4. 17
5. about 70
6. about 40
7. 9.36
8. 0.001568
9. 414,200
10. $12.90

Quiz B
Answers

1. 8.75×10^4
2. 712,000
3. 4.6
4. 2.05
5. 3.08
6. $445.84
7. 1,000
8. 500
9. 132,000
10. No, 25 tapes cost more than $60.

Glencoe Division, Macmillan/McGraw-Hill

Page 17
Cumulative Review
Answers

1. 3
2. 7
3. 18
4. 4
5. 38
6. 13
7. $11 \cdot 11$
8. 5^6
9. 17
10. 67
11. 9
12. 119
13. 0.58, 0.6, 0.89, 0.91
14. about 2,100
15. about 0.2
16. 0.034
17. 120,000
18. 1.90
19. 6.9×10^7
20. 81,600
21. 1,580
22. 0.679
23. 7.5 mi
24. missing facts
25. 6 mi

Page 18
Cumulative Test
Answers

1. A
2. B
3. C
4. A
5. D
6. C
7. D
8. A
9. B
10. D
11. D
12. D
13. A
14. B
15. D
16. A
17. A
18. D
19. A
20. C

Answer Keys, Chapter 3 Tests and Quizzes

Page 19
Form 1A
Answers

1. C
2. D
3. A
4. B
5. C
6. D
7. B
8. D
9. A
10. C
11. D
12. A
13. B

Page 20
Form 1A
Answers

14. C
15. D
16. A
17. C
18. B
19. B
20. B
    C

Page 21
Form 1B
Answers

1. B
2. D
3. C
4. D
5. A
6. C
7. A
8. B
9. D
10. B
11. A
12. A
13. C

Page 22
Form 1B
Answers

14. D
15. C
16. A
17. D
18. B
19. A
20. B
    A
    D

Answer Keys, Chapter 3 Tests and Quizzes (continued)

Page 23
Form 2A
Answers

1. **17**
2. They are equal.
3. **28**
4. **9.7**
5. Sample answer:

6.

7.

8. **11, 12; 11; 12**
9. **60; 60; 62**
10. **1.0; 1.2; 1.2**
11.
```
 7 | 67
 8 | 35
 9 | 36
10 | 69
```
12.
```
1 | 8
2 | 2678
3 | 12359
```
13. Sample answer: Between 25 and 35
14. **15, $15\frac{1}{2}$**
15. **mode**

Sample answer: The mean is the sum of the numbers divided by the number of numbers. It differs from the median in that it does not have to be a member of the set of numbers.

Page 24
Form 2B
Answers

1. **14**
2. **13**
3. **52**
4. **0.8**
5.

6.

7.

8. **22, 23; 22; 22.1**
9. **none; 8.4; 8.0**
10. **387; 432; 454**
11.
```
1 | 89
2 | 2267
3 | 07
4 | 1
```
12.
```
0 | 35
1 | 2277
2 | 006699
3 | 555
```
13.

Salary	Frequency
$20,000	6
$32,000	3
$62,500	2

14. **$31,000; $20,000; $20,000**
15. The median or mode because the two $62,500 salaries are twice as large as the mean.

Sample: 1, 2, 3, 4, 4, 4, 5, 6, 7

Page 25
Quiz A
Answers

1. $\frac{5}{40}$, or $\frac{1}{8}$
2. **$11**
3. **$2**
4. **30°F**
5. **10°F**
6. **50**
7. **21**
8. **5.5**
9.

10.

Quiz B
Answers

1. **8; 7; 6.7**
2. **88, 92; 90; 90.3**
3. **none; 13.0; 12.9**
4. **755, 805; 780; 780**
5. **2.94, 2.93, 2.94**
6. **Zoe**
7. **Maria**
8. **no**
9.
```
3 | 8
4 | 00003478
5 | 3
```
10.
```
12 | 39
13 | 2556
14 | 15
15 | 56
```

Glencoe Division, Macmillan/McGraw-Hill

Page 26
Cumulative Review
Answers

1. 51
2. 18
3. 5
4. 24
5. $8 \cdot 8 \cdot 8 \cdot 8$
6. 6^5
7. 36
8. 10
9. 2.273, 20.006 20.4, 20.44
10. 15
11. 800
12. 160
13. 70,300
14. 105,000
15. 1.27×10^8
16. 0.05
17. 8.195
18.

```
              ×
    ×   ×  ×        ×
    ×   ×  ×   ×  ×  ×
  +---+---+---+---+---+--->
   12  13 14  15  16  17
```

19. 5
20. 14
21. 14
22. 14.5
23.

2	47
3	2268
4	39
5	14
6	6

24. Sue
25. Cal

Page 27
Cumulative Test
Answers

1. A
2. C
3. B
4. A
5. D
6. C
7. A
8. B
9. C
10. D
11. D
12. C
13. A
14. A
15. B
16. C
17. B
18. C
19. D
20. C

Answer Keys, Chapter 4 Tests and Quizzes

Page 28
Form 1A
Answers

1. __B__
2. __D__
3. __C__
4. __A__
5. __C__
6. __B__
7. __A__
8. __C__
9. __B__
10. __D__
11. __A__
12. __C__
13. __C__
14. __A__

Page 29
Form 1A
Answers

15. __D__
16. __D__
17. __A__
18. __C__
19. __D__
20. __A__
21. __A__
22. __B__
23. __C__
24. __D__
25. __B__
__A__

Page 30
Form 1B
Answers

1. __A__
2 __D__
3. __B__
4. __C__
5 __D__
6 __A__
7. __B__
8. __C__
9. __A__
10. __C__
11. __B__
12. __D__
13. __C__
14. __A__

Page 31
Form 1B
Answers

15. __B__
16. __C__
17. __C__
18. __D__
19. __A__
20. __B__
21. __A__
22. __B__
23. __B__
24. __C__
25. __A__
__B__

Glencoe Division, Macmillan/McGraw-Hill

Page 32
Form 2A
Answers

1. divisible by 2, 3, 4, 6, 9
2. divisible by all
3. $3 \cdot 17$
4. $2 \cdot 7 \cdot 7$
5. $2 \cdot 2 \cdot 2 \cdot 3 \cdot 3$
6. geometric; 243, 729, 2,187
7. arithmetic; 25, 31, 37
8. 8
9. 12
10. $\frac{2}{9}$
11. $\frac{6}{7}$
12. $\frac{7}{12}$
13. 0.875
14. $\frac{7}{25}$
15. $0.\overline{63}$
16. $\frac{1}{4}$
17. $\frac{1}{2}$
18. 72
19. 360
20. >
21. >
22. $875
23. grade 8
24. divisible by 2
25. 144
$\frac{17}{19}$

Page 33
Form 2B
Answers

1. divisible by all
2. divisible by 2, 3, 4, 5, 6, 10
3. $2 \cdot 5 \cdot 13$
4. $2 \cdot 3 \cdot 3 \cdot 3 \cdot 7$
5. $2 \cdot 3 \cdot 17$
6. geometric; $\frac{1}{8}, \frac{1}{16}, \frac{1}{32}$
7. neither; 16, 22, 29
8. 6
9. 4
10. $\frac{7}{12}$
11. $\frac{8}{9}$
12. $\frac{3}{4}$
13. $0.\overline{8}$
14. $\frac{29}{50}$
15. 0.625
16. $\frac{1}{6}$
17. $\frac{5}{6}$
18. 98
19. 72
20. >
21. <
22. Cheryl
23. 75.5
24. 2, 5, 13, 34, 89
25. 5
18, 27

Page 34
Quiz A
Answers

1. divisible by all
2. divisible by all
3. $2 \cdot 2 \cdot 7$
4. $2 \cdot 2 \cdot 2 \cdot 2 \cdot 2 \cdot 2$
5. $2 \cdot 2 \cdot 2 \cdot 2 \cdot 3 \cdot 3$
6. arithmetic; 25, 31, 37
7. neither; 22, 32, 44
8. 14
9. 4
10. 1

Quiz B
Answers

1. $\frac{3}{16}$
2. $\frac{6}{5}$
3. 0.84
4. $\frac{3}{8}$
5. $\frac{1}{2}$
6. $\frac{1}{2}$
7. 72
8. 96
9. <
10. >

Glencoe Division, Macmillan/McGraw-Hill

Answer Keys, Chapter 4 Tests and Quizzes (continued)

Page 35
Cumulative Review Answers

1. 25
2. 9
3. 56
4. 18
5. 9
6. 29
7. 1,400
8. 80
9. 127,000
10. 18,000
11. 0.07
12. 9.81×10^{11}
13.
14. 5
15. 46
16. 46
17. $46.\overline{3}$
18. 79
19. divisible by 2, 3, 4, and 6
20. $2 \cdot 2 \cdot 3 \cdot 3 \cdot 3$
21. arithmetic; 30, 37, 44
22. 34, 55
23. 7; 147
24. $\frac{3}{4}$
25. $\frac{1}{2}$

Page 36
Cumulative Test Answers

1. C
2. B
3. A
4. C
5. C
6. A
7. B
8. C
9. D
10. A
11. C
12. D
13. B
14. B
15. D
16. C
17. C
18. D
19. C
20. A

Glencoe Division, Macmillan/McGraw-Hill

Answer Keys, Chapter 5 Tests and Quizzes

Page 37
Form 1A
Answers

1. _____ D
2. _____ A
3. _____ C
4. _____ B
5. _____ D
6. _____ D
7. _____ A
8. _____ C
9. _____ B
10. _____ D
11. _____ C
12. _____ C
13. _____ A

Page 38
Form 1A
Answers

14. _____ B
15. _____ C
16. _____ D
17. _____ A
18. _____ A
19. _____ C
20. _____ B
21. _____ A
22. _____ C
23. _____ C
24. _____ A
25. _____ D
_____ A

Page 39
Form 1B
Answers

1. _____ A
2. _____ C
3. _____ B
4. _____ B
5. _____ A
6. _____ B
7. _____ D
8. _____ D
9. _____ A
10. _____ C
11. _____ C
12. _____ B
13. _____ A

Page 40
Form 1B
Answers

14. _____ D
15. _____ A
16. _____ C
17. _____ C
18. _____ A
19. _____ A
20. _____ C
21. _____ D
22. _____ C
23. _____ B
24. _____ B
25. _____ D
_____ D

Glencoe Division, Macmillan/McGraw-Hill

Answer Keys, Chapter 5 Tests and Quizzes (continued)

Page 41
Form 2A
Answers

1. $2\frac{1}{4}$
2. $\frac{34}{7}$
3. $4\frac{2}{3}$
4. 3
5. 5
6. 6
7. 22
8. 21
9. $10\frac{1}{2}$
10. $1\frac{1}{40}$
11. $1\frac{20}{39}$
12. $\frac{4}{15}$
13. $\frac{1}{8}$
14. $1\frac{1}{5}$
15. $3\frac{3}{7}$
16. $6\frac{5}{6}$
17. $12\frac{17}{21}$
18. $15\frac{1}{2}$ ft
19. $1\frac{5}{28}$ mi
20. $14\frac{2}{3}$ yd
21. win
22. $3\frac{1}{2}$ cakes
23. $1\frac{7}{8}$ hours
24. $3\frac{2}{3}$ mi
25. $8.25

about 980 in.

Page 42
Form 2B
Answers

1. $13\frac{1}{2}$
2. $\frac{31}{9}$
3. $3\frac{3}{4}$
4. 5
5. 3
6. 2
7. 11
8. 26
9. $4\frac{1}{4}$
10. $1\frac{23}{36}$
11. $1\frac{17}{24}$
12. $\frac{5}{21}$
13. $\frac{2}{3}$
14. $1\frac{1}{2}$
15. $3\frac{2}{5}$
16. $6\frac{9}{20}$
17. $16\frac{13}{18}$
18. $28\frac{1}{2}$ in.
19. $2\frac{4}{9}$ yd
20. 11 ft
21. lose
22. $24\frac{1}{2}$ mi
23. about $72
24. $1\frac{3}{16}$ in.
25. $18.25

3 lb

Page 43
Quiz A

1. $11\frac{3}{4}$
2. $\frac{61}{16}$
3. 16
4. 3
5. $4\frac{5}{36}$
6. $4\frac{17}{24}$
7. $1\frac{13}{28}$
8. $\frac{11}{24}$
9. $14\frac{2}{3}$
10. $16\frac{5}{6}$ yd

Quiz B
Answers

1. $1\frac{4}{7}$ in.
2. $14\frac{1}{7}$ ft
3. win
4. lose
5. 13
6. $4\frac{1}{2}$
7. $\frac{2}{3}$
8. $5\frac{3}{5}$
9. $1\frac{2}{3}$
10. 85

Glencoe Division, Macmillan/McGraw-Hill

Page 44
Cumulative Review
Answers

1. __22__
2. __8__
3. __84__
4. __54__
5. __593__
6. __15__
7. __49.71__
8. __4,405__
9.

1	8
2	8
3	2267
4	07
5	1

10. __33__
11. __32__
12. __36__
13. __35.67__
14. __divisible by 2, 3, 4, and 6__
15. __2·2·2·2·2·3__
16. __geometric; 243, 729, 2,187__
17. __3; 45__
18. __0.583̄__
19. __$\frac{7}{12}$__
20. __$1\frac{5}{24}$__
21. __$\frac{23}{24}$__
22. __$\frac{1}{8}$__
23. __$3\frac{5}{7}$__
24. __$18\frac{1}{2}$ inches__
25. __win__

Page 45
Cumulative Test
Answers

1. __C__
2. __A__
3. __B__

4. __A__
5. __B__
6. __C__
7. __D__
8. __A__
9. __C__
10. __D__
11. __D__
12. __B__
13. __A__
14. __C__
15. __D__
16. __A__
17. __C__
18. __B__
19. __D__
20. __A__

Answer Keys, Chapter 6 Tests and Quizzes

Page 46
Form 1A
Answers

1. C
2. D
3. A
4. B
5. D
6. A
7. C
8. A
9. B
10. A
11. C
12. B
13. D
14. A

Page 47
Form 1A
Answers

15. B
16. A
17. C
18. D
19. B
20. A
21. D
22. A
23. C
24. B
25. D
C

Page 48
Form 1B
Answers

1. A
2. C
3. D
4. B
5. A
6. C
7. C
8. A
9. B
10. D
11. A
12. C
13. B
14. D

Page 49
Form 1B
Answers

15. D
16. B
17. A
18. C
19. C
20. A
21. D
22. A
22.. D
24. B
25. C
D

Glencoe Division, Macmillan/McGraw-Hill

Answer Keys, Chapter 6 Tests and Quizzes (continued)

Page 50
Form 2A
Answers

1. 7.3
2. 5.13
3. 3.2
4. 27
5. 34
6. $18\frac{5}{6}$
7. 11.5
8. 17
9. 60
10. 0.5
11. $\frac{3}{4}$
12. $z + 12$
13. $l - 10$
14. $13y$
15. $d \div 5$
16. 3
17. 0.5
18. 80 oz
19. 6 pt
20. 2.76 mm^2
21. 21 yd^2
22. 22.1 cm^2
23. 84 ft^2
24. 21
25. $27,000
Jami is 4 years younger than Rita, or Rita is 4 years older than Jami.

Page 51
Form 2B
Answers

1. 13.2
2. 3.2
3. $9\frac{3}{4}$
4. 7
5. 31
6. 6.5
7. $18\frac{3}{4}$
8. 80
9. 12
10. 0.05
11. $\frac{2}{5}$
12. $20 - j$
13. $x + 3$
14. $\frac{f}{9}$
15. $2t$
16. 1
17. 2
18. 10
19. 3,000 lb
20. 2.64 cm^2
21. 40.5 ft^2
22. 119.48 ft^2
23. 8 ft
24. 1,164 points
25. 4 pitchers
48 years

Page 52
Quiz A
Answers

1. 432
2. $2\frac{1}{4}$
3. 15
4. 122
5. $24\frac{5}{8}$
6. 9
7. 7.8
8. 3
9. $s + 9$
10. $n - 12$

Quiz B
Answers

1. 3.5
2. 3.5
3. 24
4. 2.5
5. 5.5
6. 3.91 mm^2
7. 6.63 cm^2
8. 8 yd
9. 5.5
10. 3 guards

Glencoe Division, Macmillan/McGraw-Hill

Answer Keys, Chapter 6 Tests and Quizzes (continued)

Page 53
Cumulative Review
Answers

1. _____ **12** _____

2. _____ **0.06** _____

3.

4. _____ **4** _____

5. _____ **36** _____

6. _____ **36** _____

7. _____ **35.3** _____

8. _____ neither; **36, 49, 64** _____

9. _____ **8; 120** _____

10. _____ **$0.\overline{6}$** _____

11. _____ **$\frac{7}{8}$** _____

12. _____ **$\frac{1}{4}$** _____

13. _____ **$\frac{9}{20}$** _____

14. _____ **$2\frac{1}{5}$ mi** _____

15. _____ **18.5 ft** _____

16. _____ **8.635 mm** _____

17. _____ **$y - 10$** _____

18. _____ **11 pt** _____

19. _____ **24.5 ft^2** _____

20. _____ **$1\frac{7}{45}$** _____

21. _____ **$6\frac{8}{9}$** _____

22. _____ **$\frac{7}{8}$** _____

23. _____ **2.1** _____

24. _____ **3** _____

25. _____ **$1\frac{3}{4}$** _____

Page 54
Cumulative Test
Answers

1. _____ **C** _____

2. _____ **D** _____

3. _____ **B** _____

4. _____ **A** _____

5. _____ **D** _____

6. _____ **C** _____

7. _____ **A** _____

8. _____ **C** _____

9. _____ **D** _____

10. _____ **B** _____

11. _____ **A** _____

12. _____ **C** _____

13. _____ **D** _____

14. _____ **B** _____

15. _____ **C** _____

16. _____ **D** _____

17. _____ **A** _____

18. _____ **C** _____

19. _____ **B** _____

20. _____ **A** _____

Glencoe Division, Macmillan/McGraw-Hill

Answer Keys, Chapter 7 Tests and Quizzes

Page 55
Form 1A
Answers

1. B
2. A
3. B
4. C
5. D
6. C
7. B
8. D
9. A
10. C
11. D
12. B
13. D

Page 56
Form 1A
Answers

14. B
15. D
16. B
17. C
18. B
19. A
20. B
21. C
22. A
23. D
24. A
25. D
A

Page 57
Form 1B
Answers

1. C
2. B
3. A
4. D
5. C
6. D
7. A
8. B
9. A
10. D
11. B
12. C
13. A
14. A

Page 58
Form 1B
Answers

15. C
16. D
17. A
18. B
19. C
20. C
21. A
22. C
23. D
24. B
25. C
C

Glencoe Division, Macmillan/McGraw-Hill

Page 59
Form 2A
Answers

1. $-2; 2; 2$
2. $-6; 6; 6$
3. $4; -4; 4$
4. $<$
5. $>$
6. $<$
7. St. Paul
8. See graph.
9. See graph.
10. See graph.
11. See graph.
12. 4
13. -33
14. -7
15. 0
16. 56
17. 9
18. -45
19. -6
20. 18
21. -9
22. -15
23. -24
24. 3
25. 5
26. $10:39$
27. 0.0006
28. 5×10^{-6}
29. $0.2x = -1.6; -8$
30. 0.00009
$51; 66$

Page 60
Form 2B
Answers

1. $5; -5; 5$
2. $0; 0; 0$
3. $-3; 3; 3$
4. $<$
5. $>$
6. $>$
7. Boise
8. See graph.
9. See graph.
10. See graph.
11. See graph.
12. 4
13. 72
14. -7
15. 0
16. -63
17. 25
18. -32
19. -9
20. 16
21. -2
22. -12
23. -36
24. 3
25. 5
26. 27 sit-ups
27. 0.005
28. 3×10^{-7}
29. $e + (-6) = 13; 19$
30. May 29
$2,500$

Page 61
Quiz A
Answers

1. $19; 19$
2. $-25; 25$
3. $-4, -2, -1, 0, 3, 4$
4. See graph
5. See graph
6. See graph
7. -37
8. -3
9. -57
10. 32

Quiz B
Answers

1. 98
2. -96
3. 4
4. -20
5. -112
6. -100
7. $k \div (-4) = -11; 44$
8. 0.0000002
9. 2×10^{-9}
10. $10:36$

Page 62
Cumulative Review
Answers

1. 25
2. 1, 1.01, 1.10, 10.1, 11.1
3. 2.07×10^9
4. 7 and 11
5. 9
6. 9
7. arithmetic; 55, 49, 43
8. $0.8\overline{3}$
9. $\frac{1}{8}$
10. $\frac{3}{10}$
11. $\frac{7}{20}$
12. 22 yards
13. 6 times
14. $1\frac{4}{7}$ inches
15. $\frac{c}{11}$
16. 14 quarts
17. 103.7 cm^2
18. 10:42
19. $0.3t = -0.63$; -2.1
20. $1\frac{11}{24}$
21. $\frac{2}{3}$
22. $2\frac{15}{16}$
23. 4
24. -144
25. -4

Page 63
Cumulative Test
Answers

1. A
2. B
3. C
4. D
5. D
6. A
7. B
8. C
9. D
10. A
11. D
12. C
13. B
14. A
15. C
16. C
17. A
18. C
19. B
20. C

162

Answer Keys, Chapter 8 Tests and Quizzes

Page 64
Form 1A
Answers

1. A
2. B
3. C
4. A
5. D
6. C
7. B
8. A
9. C
10. A
11. D
12. A

Page 65
Form 1A
Answers

13. D
14. B
15. C
16. A
17. B
18. D
19. A
20. D

C

Page 66
Form 1B
Answers

1. D
2. A
3. B
4. B
5. D
6. A
7. D
8. C
9. A
10. D
11. B
12. C

Page 67
Form 1B
Answers

13. B
14. D
15. C
16. D
17. A
18. C
19. A
20. D

D

Glencoe Division, Macmillan/McGraw-Hill

Page 68
Form 2A
Answers

1. acute
2. obtuse
3. straight
4. right
5. No, because not all sides are segments.
6. No, because some sides meet at places other than endpoints
7. yes
8. scalene, obtuse
9. scalene, right
10. isosceles, obtuse
11. trapezoid
12. parallelogram, rhombus, rectangle, square; square
13. parallelogram, rectangle; rectangle
14. yes
15. No, because all sides are not the same length.
16. No, because the angles do not have the same measure.
17. no
18. yes
19. yes
20.
21.
22. Check students' drawings; 4
23.
24.
25. Amy, Oct.; Bucky, July; Lucy, Jan.; Jamie, Dec. If 360 is divisible by the angle measure, the polygon will tessellate.

Page 69
Form 2B
Answers

1. right
2. acute
3. obtuse
4. straight
5. yes
6. No, because it is not a closed figure
7. No, because there are no sides.
8. scalene, obtuse
9. equilateral, acute
10. isosceles, right
11. quadrilateral
12. parallelogram, rhombus; rhombus
13. parallelogram
14. yes
15. yes
16. No, because all sides are not the same length.
17. no
18. yes
19. no
20.
21.
22. Check students' drawings; 3
23.
24.
25. Rino, pear; Ada, orange; Jessup, apple

Page 70
Quiz A
Answers

1. obtuse
2. straight
3. acute
4. yes
5. No, because it is not a closed figure
6. isosceles, acute
7. scalene, right
8. parallelogram, rectangle; rectangle
9. parallelogram
10. No; in general, the angles aren't all congruent.

Quiz B
Answers

1. yes
2. no
3. yes
4. yes
5.
6.
7.
8.
9.
10. brown

Page 71
Cumulative Review
Answers

1. 43
2. 187,000
3. 50
4. $22\frac{1}{3}$
5. geometric; 243, 729, 2,187
6. $0.\overline{5}$
7. 9; 126
8. 16 yd
9. $z + 12$
10. 13.5 mi^2
11. 82, 37
12. $\frac{r}{0.5} = -0.76; -0.38$
13. $9\frac{13}{24}$
14. $5\frac{17}{40}$
15. 8
16. $8\frac{5}{12}$
17. 7.5
18. -57
19. -212
20. 356
21. acute
22. scalene, obtuse
23. isosceles, acute
24. parallelogram
25. parallelogram, rhombus, rectangle, square; square

Page 72
Cumulative Test
Answers

1. A
2. C
3. D
4. B
5. C
6. A
7. A
8. D
9. C
10. C
11. D
12. C
13. A
14. B
15. A
16. C
17. B
18. A
19. B
20. D

Answer Keys, Chapter 9 Tests and Quizzes

Page 73
Form 1A
Answers

1. C
2. D
3. A
4. B
5. D
6. A
7. C
8. C
9. A
10. C
11. B
12. D

Page 74
Form 1A
Answers

13. C
14. D
15. C
16. D
17. A
18. C
19. C
20. A

C

Page 75
Form 1B
Answers

1. A
2. D
3. A
4. C
5. D
6. C
7. C
8. B
9. A
10. D
11. A
12. B

Page 76
Form 1B
Answers

13. A
14. C
15. C
16. D
17. C
18. A
19. B
20. C

C

Answer Keys, Chapter 9 Tests and Quizzes (continued)

Page 77
Form 2A
Answers

1. 50, 40
2. 17
3. 14
4. 14
5. 64
6. 225
7. 400
8. 20 m
9. 18 cm
10. 6.2 ft
11. 12 ft
12. 14 miles
13. 20.5 units^2
14. 19 units^2
15. 360 m^2
16. 576 cm^2
17. 615.44 in^2
18. 907.46 m^2
19. $\frac{1}{5}$
20. $\frac{1}{6}$

121.5 mm^2

Page 78
Form 2B
Answers

1. 30, 32
2. 16
3. 21
4. 11
5. 144
6. 49
7. 1,600
8. 25 m
9. 40 cm
10. 8.5 ft
11. 100 m
12. 24 ft
13. 16.5 units^2
14. 20 units^2
15. 500 mm^2
16. 720 m^2
17. 1,017.36 cm^2
18. 1,384.74 in^2
19. $\frac{3}{10}$
20. $\frac{1}{5}$

11.44 cm^2

Page 79
Quiz A
Answers

1. 60, 40
2. 6
3. 19
4. 70
5. 8
6. 12
7. 15
8. 50 ft
9. 7.9 cm
10. 20 ft

Quiz B
Answers

1. 12.5 units^2
2. 20 units^2
3. 3,840 m^2
4. 2,400 mm^2
5. 792 ft^2
6. 50.24 ft^2
7. 1,133.54 m^2
8. 10.1736 m^2
9. $\frac{1}{5}$
10. $\frac{2}{15}$

Glencoe Division, Macmillan/McGraw-Hill

Answer Keys, Chapter 9 Tests and Quizzes (continued)

Page 80
Cumulative Review
Answers

1. 9
2. 1,296
3. 140
4. 590
5. 8.7×10^8
6.

  30 31 32 33 34 35 36

7. 3
8. 36
9. 35
10. 35
11. $2 \cdot 2 \cdot 2 \cdot 3 \cdot 5$
12. 6; 420
13. $\frac{1}{6}$
14. $1\frac{8}{9}$
15. $3\frac{8}{15}$
16. 3
17. -6
18. -161
19. 9,000
20. 60
21. obtuse
22. scalene, right
23. 13
24. 50 ft
25. 1,661.06 ft^2

Page 81
Cumulative Test
Answers

1. C
2. B
3. D
4. B
5. C
6. A
7. D
8. C
9. C
10. C
11. A
12. B
13. C
14. B
15. C
16. B
17. B
18. B
19. D
20. A

Glencoe Division, Macmillan/McGraw-Hill

Answer Keys, Chapter 10 Tests and Quizzes

Page 82
Form 1A
Answers

1. ___D___

2. ___C___

3. ___A___

4. ___C___

5. ___B___

6. ___A___

7. ___D___

Page 83
Form 1A
Answers

8. ___A___

9. ___A___

10. ___C___

11. ___A___

12. ___D___

13. ___A___

14. ___A___

15. ___B___

___B___

Page 84
Form 1B
Answers

1. ___B___

2. ___A___

3. ___D___

4. ___B___

5. ___A___

6. ___D___

7. ___A___

Page 85
Form 1B
Answers

8. ___C___

9. ___A___

10. ___C___

11. ___B___

12. ___A___

13. ___A___

14. ___B___

15. ___C___

___D___

Glencoe Division, Macmillan/McGraw-Hill

Page 86
Form 2A
Answers

1.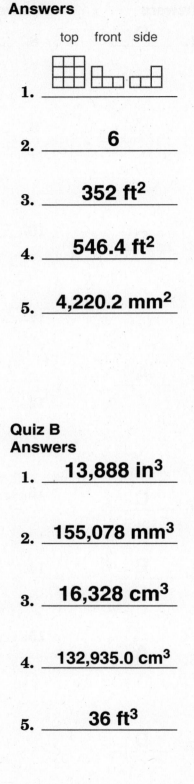

2.

3. top   front   side

4. top   front   side

5. **622 ft²**

6. **159.3 cm²**

7. **816.4 mm²**

8. **56.3 ft²**

9. **4**

10. **6,480 mm³**

11. **10,080 ft³**

12. **20,790 cm³**

13. **16,016 in³**

14. **53⅓ yd³**

15. **56.5 in³**

729 in³

Page 87
Form 2B
Answers

1.

2.

3. top   front   side

4. top   front   side

5. **3,160 cm²**

6. **37½ in²**

7. **2,198 ft²**

8. **3,899.9 mm²**

9. **3**

10. **40,320 cm³**

11. **7,020 in³**

12. **385,000 mm³**

13. **1,078 cm³**

14. **810 ft³**

15. **138.16 in³**

343 cm³

Page 88
Quiz A
Answers

top   front   side

1.

2. **6**

3. **352 ft²**

4. **546.4 ft²**

5. **4,220.2 mm²**

Quiz B
Answers

1. **13,888 in³**

2. **155,078 mm³**

3. **16,328 cm³**

4. **132,935.0 cm³**

5. **36 ft³**

Page 89
Cumulative Review
Answers

1. 22
2. 0.005
3. 89
4. $0.41\overline{6}$
5. 36
6. $3\frac{11}{12}$
7. $2\frac{1}{2}$
8. $7\frac{1}{2}$
9. $5\frac{11}{16}$
10. 9.3
11. -12
12. -132
13. 81
14. acute
15. parallelogram, rhombus
16. 50, 52
17. 20
18. no
19. 123.25 ft^2
20. 240 ft^2
21. 706.5 ft^2
22. 6,904 mm^2
23. 1,526.04 cm^2
24. 30,100 mm^3
25. 4,578.12 cm^3

Page 90
Cumulative Test
Answers

1. B
2. C
3. B
4. A
5. C
6. C
7. D
8. A
9. C
10. C
11. B
12. B
13. B
14. A
15. D

Glencoe Division, Macmillan/McGraw-Hill

Answer Keys, Chapter 11 Tests and Quizzes

Page 91
Form 1A
Answers

1. D
2. C
3. B
4. B
5. C
6. B
7. A
8. C
9. D

Page 92
Form 1A
Answers

10. D
11. C
12. A
13. B
14. A
15. A
16. C
17. C
18. C
19. D
20. C

B

Page 93
Form 1B
Answers

1. A
2. C
3. C
4. B
5. D
6. A
7. D
8. C
9. D

Page 94
Form 1B
Answers

10. A
11. A
12. D
13. B
14. A
15. C
16. B
17. B
18. C
19. A
20. C

A

Page 95
Form 2A
Answers

1. $\frac{20}{3}$
2. 9.6 miles per hour
3. 8.75
4. $9\frac{1}{3}$
5. 32.2
6. $2\frac{2}{5}$ in. by $4\frac{4}{5}$ in.
7. 13%
8. 27.5%
9. 37.5%
10. 8.5%
11. $466\frac{2}{3}\%$
12. $\frac{1}{25}$
13. $\frac{1}{9}$
14. 0.073
15. 2.78
16. 0.000049
17. <
18. =
19. 18
20. $53.69
0.000000000000054

Page 96
Form 2B
Answers

1. $\frac{4}{1}$
2. $0.53 per pound
3. 2.25
4. 7.2
5. 3.375
6. $1\frac{1}{3}$ in. by $1\frac{1}{2}$ in.
7. 12%
8. 19.4%
9. 62.5%
10. 4.5%
11. $233\frac{1}{3}\%$
12. $\frac{1}{20}$
13. $\frac{4}{9}$
14. 0.085
15. 5.77
16. 0.000036
17. >
18. <
19. 6 stops
20. 621 students
8

Page 97
Quiz A
Answers

1. $\frac{6}{1}$
2. $\frac{3}{13}$
3. $0.29 per pound
4. 16 meters per second
5. 5
6. 9.6
7. 1.25
8. 25.2
9. 150 miles
10. 525 miles

Quiz B
Answers

1. 24%
2. 7.9%
3. $58\frac{1}{3}\%$
4. $\frac{31}{200}$
5. 53.2%
6. 1,350%
7. 0.007
8. 240%
9. =
10. 243

Page 98
Cumulative Review
Answers

1. ___150___

2. ___15___

3. ___$\frac{5}{6}$___

4. ___$\frac{13}{18}$___

5. ___$\frac{2}{3}$___

6. ___67.16 ft^2___

7. ___216___

8. ___-4___

9. ___scalene, right___

10. ___equilateral, acute___

11. ___false___

12. ___7.8 cm___

13. ___168 ft^2___

14. ___288 ft^2___

15. ___361.12 mm^2___

16. ___1846.32 ft^2___

17. ___739.26 yd^2___

18. ___28.5 miles per gallon___

19. ___19.2___

20. ___38.64%___

Page 99
Cumulative Test
Answers

1. ___B___

2. ___C___

3. ___D___

4. ___C___

5. ___A___

6. ___C___

7. ___A___

8. ___B___

9. ___A___

10. ___C___

11. ___C___

12. ___D___

13. ___D___

14. ___B___

15. ___A___

Glencoe Division, Macmillan/McGraw-Hill

Answer Keys, Chapter 12 Tests and Quizzes

Page 100
Form 1A
Answers

1. __B__
2. __C__
3. __B__
4. __D__
5. __B__
6. __C__
7. __A__
8. __D__

9. __B__

10. __B__

Page 101
Form 1A
Answers

11. __A__
12. __A__
13. __A__
14. __C__
15. __D__
16. __D__
17. __C__
18. __B__

19. __A__

20. __D__

__A__

Page 102
Form 1B
Answers

1. __B__
2. __D__
3. __C__
4. __C__
5. __D__
6. __B__
7. __B__
8. __B__

9. __D__

10. __D__

Page 103
Form 1B
Answers

11. __B__
12. __C__
13. __B__
14. __A__
15. __C__
16. __D__
17. __A__
18. __B__

19. __C__

20. __B__

__D__

Glencoe Division, Macmillan/McGraw-Hill

Page 104
Form 2A
Answers

1. 36.6
2. 60.8
3. 2
4. 15.5
5. 163.2
6. 82%
7. Fish
8. 11%
9. 57%
10. $45.60
11. $437.50
12. $54.15
13. 13 hours
14. 61%
15. $75.35
    187, 188, 189, or 190

Page 105
Form 2B
Answers

1. 8.7
2. 41.2
3. 75
4. 14.3
5. 8.7
6. 216%
7. Black
8. 28%
9. 11%
10. $23.70
11. $6.38
12. $671.33
13. 25 lawns
14. 44%
15. $73.90
    $17.50

Page 106
Quiz A
Answers

1. 37.7
2. 4.25
3. 120
4. 4
5. 400
6. 380%
7. 98.5
8. 4.4
9. 77
10. about 75,000

Quiz B
Answers

1. 0.27
2. 97°
3. 14%
4. $118.99
5. $161.78

Page 107
Cumulative Review
Answers

1. 1,270

2. $2 \cdot 2 \cdot 3 \cdot 3 \cdot 5$

3. $11\frac{5}{6}$ ft

4. 25

5. -5; 5; 5

6. obtuse

7. No; not all sides are segments.

8. 17

9. 8

10. 56.7 cm²

11. 126.0 in²

12. 264 m³

13. 668.8 mm³

14. $\frac{8}{11}$

15. 5

16. 1.75 inches

17. 0.0345

18. about 6

19. 33%

20. $577.50

Page 108
Cumulative Test
Answers

1. D

2. A

3. B

4. A

5. A

6. D

7. A

8. C

9. D

10. D

11. B

12. C

13. C

14. D

15. A

Answer Keys, Chapter 13 Tests and Quizzes

Page 109
Form 1A
Answers

1. __C__
2. __A__
3. __D__
4. __B__
5. __C__
6. __B__
7. __D__
8. __B__
9. __C__

Page 110
Form 1A
Answers

10. __A__
11. __D__
12. __A__
13. __D__
14. __A__
15. __C__
16. __A__
17. __A__
18. __C__
19. __D__
20. __B__

__D__

Page 111
Form 1B
Answers

1. __D__
2. __C__
3. __A__
4. __A__
5. __C__
6. __C__
7. __A__
8. __B__
9. __B__

Page 112
Form 1B
Answers

10. __D__
11. __A__
12. __C__
13. __D__
14. __A__
15. __C__
16. __A__
17. __C__
18. __B__
19. __B__
20. __B__

__C__

Page 113
Form 2A
Answers

1. ___**24**___

2. ___**36 faces**___

3. ___$\frac{1}{3}$___

4. ___$\frac{5}{6}$___

5. ___**1**___

6. ___**24%**___

7. ___**Russell**___

8. ___$\frac{1}{30}$___

9. ___$\frac{1}{25}$___

10. ___**1**___

11. ___**30**___

12. ___**840**___

13. ___**4**___

14. ___**6 ways**___

15. ___**56**___

___**1**___

Page 114
Form 2B
Answers

1. ___**6**___

2. ___**12**___

3. ___$\frac{1}{3}$___

4. ___$\frac{1}{6}$___

5. ___**1**___

6. ___**28%**___

7. ___**Warren**___

8. ___$\frac{1}{24}$___

9. ___$\frac{1}{25}$___

10. ___**120**___

11. ___**72**___

12. ___**5**___

13. ___**10**___

14. ___**40,320 ways**___

15. ___**15 ways**___

___**17,576**___

Page 115
Quiz A
Answers

1. ___**24**___

2. ___**50**___

3. ___$\frac{4}{25}$___

4. ___$\frac{1}{6}$___

5. ___$\frac{2}{5}$___

Quiz B
Answers

1. ___**22%**___

2. ___**2,310 people**___

3. ___$\frac{1}{8}$___

4. ___$\frac{5}{8}$___

5. ___**2**___

6. ___**12**___

7. ___**60,480**___

8. ___**56**___

9. ___**5,040**___

10. ___**840**___

Glencoe Division, Macmillan/McGraw-Hill

Page 116
Cumulative Review
Answers

1. 43
2. 5
3. $\frac{17}{24}$
4. 57
5. 126
6. parallelogram, rectangle
7. 7.9 units
8. 256
9. 30.6 in^2
10. 692.37 cm^3
11. 73.12 yd^2
12. 24 miles per gallon
13. 0.77
14. 86%
15. 69°
16. $9.95
17. 5
18. 84
19. 403 students
20. $\frac{9}{25}$

Page 117
Cumulative Test
Answers

1. C
2. C
3. A
4. A
5. C
6. D
7. B
8. A
9. C
10. A
11. D
12. C
13. B
14. D
15. B

Answer Keys, Chapter 14 Tests and Quizzes

Page 118
Form 1A
Answers

1. **B**
2. **C**
3. **C**
4. **D**
5. **B**
6. **C**
7. **B**
8. **C**
9. **D**
10. **A**
11. **C**

Page 119
Form 1A
Answers

12. **D**
13. **D**
14. **B**
15. **D**
16. **A**
17. **C**
18. **A**
19. **D**
20. **B**
    D

Page 120
Form 1B
Answers

1. **B**
2. **D**
3. **C**
4. **C**
5. **A**
6. **A**
7. **D**
8. **C**
9. **C**
10. **D**
11. **C**

Page 121
Form 1B
Answers

12. **B**
13. **C**
14. **A**
15. **D**
16. **B**
17. **D**
18. **B**
19. **A**
20. **D**
    B

Glencoe Division, Macmillan/McGraw-Hill

Page 122
Form 2A
Answers

1. _____ 1 ounce _____

2. _____ 6 _____

3. _____ 1.1 _____

4. _____ 10 _____

5. _____ (−1, 5); (0, 2); (1, −1); (2, −4) _____

6. _____ (−1, −7); (0, −3); (1, 1); (2, 5) _____

7. _____ $y = 0.50x + 3$ _____

8. _____ See graph. _____

9. _____ See graph. _____

10. _____ $y = 3x − 7$ _____

11. _____ −12, 4, 8, 12 _____

12. _____ 16, 10, 4, −2 _____

13. _____ See graph. _____

14. _____ See graph. _____

15. _____ See graph. _____
$y = 4 − 2x$

Page 123
Form 2B
Answers

1. _____ 8,400 shares _____

2. _____ 4 _____

3. _____ −3.8 _____

4. _____ −21 _____

5. _____ (−1, −7), (0, −2), (1, 3), (2, 8) _____

6. _____ (−2, 2), (0, 3), (2, 4), (4, 5) _____

7. _____ $y = 50 + x$ _____

8. _____ See graph. _____

9. _____ See graph. _____

10. _____ $y = 5x + 2$ _____

11. _____ −10, 0, 10, 20 _____

12. _____ −4, −3.5, −2.5, −2 _____

13. _____ See graph. _____

14. _____ See graph. _____

15. _____ See graph. _____
$y = 7x − 17$

Page 124
Quiz A
Answers

1. _____ 2.5 gallons _____

2. _____ 3 _____

3. _____ 0.5 _____

4. _____ (−1, 1); (0, 3); (1, 5); (2, 7) _____

5. _____ (−3, −4); (0, −3); (3, −2); (6, −1) _____

Quiz B
Answers

1. _____ See graph. _____

2. _____ $y = −3x − 2$ _____

3. _____ See graph. _____

4. _____ −5, −6, −7, −8 _____

5. _____ See graph. _____

Glencoe Division, Macmillan/McGraw-Hill

**Page 125
Cumulative Review
Answers**

1. __0.201__
2. __2, 3, 5, 6, 10__
3. __31__
4.
5. __40.5 mm^2__
6.
7. __3,450 ft^3__
8. __0.021%__
9. __10.08__
10. __$16\frac{2}{3}$%__
11. __900 miles__
12. __565.25__
13. __31.74__
14. __$624__
15. __30__
16. __12__
17. __$\frac{1}{4}$__
18. __3.5__
19. __(−1, −6), (0, −4), (1, −2), (2, 0)__
20. __2, 6, 8, 10__

**Page 126
Cumulative Test
Answers**

1. __A__
2. __D__
3. __C__
4. __C__
5. __D__
6. __C__
7. __D__
8. __D__
9. __A__
10. __B__
11. __A__
12. __C__
13. __A__
14. __B__
15. __D__

Answer Keys, Semester Tests

Page 127
Form 1
Answers

1. D
2. A
3. B
4. C
5. C
6. A
7. D
8. C
9. B
10. D
11. A
12. C
13. B
14. A
15. C

Page 128
Form 1
Answers

16. A
17. C
18. B
19. C
20. A
21. C
22. D
23. D
24. A
25. C
26. B
27. C
28. C
29. A

Page 129
Form 1
Answers

30. D
31. C
32. B
33. C
34. A
35. B
36. C
37. B
38. C
39. B
40. D
41. A
42. D
43. B

Page 130
Form 1
Answers

44. D
45. C
46. D
47. A
48. C
49. A
50. A

Glencoe Division, Macmillan/McGraw-Hill

Answer Keys, Semester Tests (continued)

Page 131
Form 2
Answers

1. 600
2. 11
3. 28
4. 729
5. 80
6. 7
7. The cost of the large pizza is a missing fact.
8. 2.74, 2.53, 0.91, 0.9
9. 3.468
10. 1,500
11. 761,000
12. 0.415
13. 0.95
14. $247.50
15. 70 72 74 76 78 80
16. 23 24 25 26 27
17. 4; 26; 26; 25.1
18.
$$\begin{array}{c|c} 1 & 3 \\ 2 & 3477 \\ 3 & 125 \\ 4 & 26 \end{array}$$
19. See students' work.
20. $30,000; $30,000; $41,000

Page 132
Form 2
Answers

21. The mode or median since the two $72,500 salaries are about $42,000 larger than the mean.
22. divisible by all
23. geometric; 512, 2,048, 8,192
24. 12; 72
25. $\frac{2}{3}$
26. $0.\overline{54}$
27. $\frac{5}{8}$
28. $\frac{1}{2}$
29. $1,000
30. 2
31. $1\frac{13}{18}$
32. $\frac{1}{9}$
33. $5\frac{19}{21}$
34. $18\frac{1}{2}$ yd
35. 2.355 ft
36. lose
37. 7.8

Page 133
Form 2
Answers

38. $15\frac{1}{6}$
39. $2\frac{1}{3}$
40. $k + 13$
41. 5.78 cm^2
42. 663 mm^2
43. 4
44. See graph.
45. See graph.
46. −28
47. 4
48. 5
49. 6.3×10^{-7}
50. 36 sit-ups

Glencoe Division, Macmillan/McGraw-Hill

Answer Keys, Final Tests

1. __C__
2. __D__
3. __B__
4. __C__
5. __A__
6. __C__
7. __D__
8. __A__
9. __B__
10. __B__
11. __D__
12. __D__

13. __A__
14. __A__
15. __C__
16. __D__
17. __A__
18. __D__
19. __A__
20. __D__
21. __B__
22. __C__
23. __B__
24. __C__
25. __C__
26. __A__

27. __B__
28. __A__
29. __A__
30. __B__
31. __B__
32. __B__
33. __C__
34. __A__
35. __D__
36. __C__
37. __C__
38. __B__

Answer Keys, Final Tests (continued)

39. __C__

40. __B__

41. __A__

42. __A__

43. __C__

44. __B__

45. __D__

46. __B__

47. __C__

48. __B__

49. __D__

50. __A__

51. __D__

52. __A__

53. __B__

54. __C__

55. __D__

56. __C__

57. __C__

58. __A__

59. __C__

60. __D__

Glencoe Division, Macmillan/McGraw-Hill

Page 139
Form 2
Answers

1. 13
2. 27
3. 0.03, 0.32, 0.37, 3.4
4. 390
5. 5
6. 58
7. 120
8. 1
9. $1\frac{1}{2}$
10. $2\frac{5}{14}$ yards
11. 3
12. 17 quarts
13. 57.66 m²
14. −4; 4; 4
15. 4
16. 0.0005
17. acute
18. pentagon
19. scalene, right

Page 140
Form 2
Answers

20.
21. 7
22. no
23. 85.5 cm²
24. 23.75 mm²
25. 2.2 feet
26.
27. 2,034.72 in²
28. 105 ft³
29. 43.96 in³
30. 84.78 in³
31. 6.25
32. 4.5 people/car
33. 13.3
34. 0.545
35. 0.75%
36. 828
37. 10%

Page 141
Form 2
Answers

38. $13.97
39. $21.20
40. $375
41. 60 outfits
42. $\frac{1}{12}$
43. $\frac{5}{76}$
44. 360
45. 84
46. −8
47. $170
48. See graph.
49. −7, −3, −1, 1
50. See graph.